Nature and Human Nature

Nature and Human Nature

MAN'S NEW IMAGE OF HIMSELF

by Lawrence K. Frank

1951

RUTGERS UNIVERSITY PRESS

NEW BRUNSWICK, NEW JERSEY

Manufactured in the United States of America

Preface

THIS VOLUME IS OFFERED AS AN interpretation of recently developed conceptions and new ways of thinking about Nature and human nature. As the introductory and the concluding chapters point out, we are living in a time of extraordinary changes, going far beyond any previous periods in our western history or that of any other people.

These changes in all our customary ways of living, the revolutionary upheavals which have been occurring more and more frequently, and often violently, may be interpreted as so many diverse expressions of the underlying and profound alteration in our ideas about nature and man. At least it may be said that until we grasp these new ideas and recognize the new climate of opinion they are bringing, our understanding of what is happening to us and to all other people will be greatly limited and subject to all the contending schools of thought that now are offering their simple explanation and utopian remedies.

The materials in this volume were first presented in an abbreviated form in an article entitled "Man's Multi-dimensional Environment," published in the *Scientific Monthly*, April, 1943.* Later, at the invitation of Dr. Houston Peterson, then Director of the Cooper Union Forum (to whom I am indebted for his encouragement and assistance in publishing this and a previous book), the contents of this paper were given in a series of four lectures in January, 1946, as part of the series entitled *Prometheus Unbound.*

The notes of those lectures were later revised and enlarged with the addition of introductory and concluding chapters, to round out the presentation and to indicate the relevance and, in the writer's opinion, the great significance of these new ideas and the new way of thinking they now make possible. What is of special significance is that today we can formulate a conception of nature and human nature, of their operations, including the development of culture and social order and the emergence of personality, with the same basic assumptions. Thus we need not invoke various *ad hoc* agents and forces or unnatural entities in order to provide a consistent, dynamic interpretation of nature, human nature, culture, society and the individual personality, as different expressions of the same dynamic circular processes.

As the final chapter suggests, we face an extraordinary task of re-orientating ourselves toward nature and man, revising our traditional beliefs and assumptions and, with the new conceptions and the new criteria of credibility we are developing today, of renewing our culture and reconstructing our social order within a world community. For this we need a new image of man, a new conception of human potentialities.

As also pointed out, we have as guiding purposes in this great labor our enduring goals and the aspirations toward which

---

* Now available in the writer's volume, *Society as the Patient,* Rutgers University Press, 1948.

all of our previous religion, philosophy, law, morals and ethics have been directed—the worth of the human personality and the dignity of man, woman and child.

With a firm conviction that these are central and that today they can be asserted without reliance upon non-human or super-human sanctions, we can courageously accept this task, confident that both nature and man, as we are now recognizing, provide the basic foundations for achieving these goals and aspirations.

To those who are confused and perplexed in the midst of the contemporary situation and the growing contentiousness, this small volume is offered as a way of understanding and interpreting the new knowledge and insights recently developed concerning nature and man. What is presented here is not offered as a pronouncement, but, as repeatedly stated, it is an attempt to show how a new way of thinking may enable us to meet our present difficulties constructively and hopefully.

It will be apparent that the writer has drawn upon many sources and individuals for what is herein presented. No attempt has been made to indicate these by specific references since it would be difficult, if not impossible, to cite all the books and papers, the lectures and the discussions that have contributed to this presentation. I am especially indebted to Gregory Bateson, Harold Taylor and my son Alan Frank, for many helpful criticisms and constructive suggestions.

Elsewhere the writer has stated and elaborated some of the themes of this volume, and readers are referred to these other publications* for further leads.

LAWRENCE K. FRANK

Cloverly
Ashland, New Hampshire

* *Society as the Patient,* Rutgers University Press, 1948; and *Projective Methods,* Charles C. Thomas, 1948.

Contents

Nature and Human Nature

I

Our New Climate of Opinion

IN THE MIDST OF ALL THE TUR-
moil and confusion, the widespread conflict and strife all over
the world, it is difficult for us to realize what is taking place
today, and almost impossible for us to understand these stirring
events.

It may help us to gain some perspective, to anticipate, so
far as we can do so, the interpretation which future historians
may give to this troubled era.

Undoubtedly for centuries to come the historians, as well
as other students of social life and of art and literature, will be
engaged in vigorous disputes over what did happen in the first
half of the twentieth century and what it all meant. Just as there
are various schools of thought about what we call the past, so

those who come after us will almost surely differ widely in what they think about their past—our present.

They will probably agree on one characteristic of our present time: that it was (is) a revolutionary period, a time when in almost every field of activity and of ideas, new patterns and new conceptions are being developed to challenge the old and, with sometimes extraordinary rapidity, to supersede the long accustomed ways of living, thinking and believing.

As we grope around and attempt to understand this period that has been called the beginning of a continuing revolution, we may recall two other periods in Western European life when there were somewhat similar changes taking place, namely classical Greece and the Renaissance.

In the sixth and fifth centuries in Greece, there arose a spirit of inquiry, a new and critical attitude toward tradition. Men began to question immemorial customs and ages-old beliefs, asking if they were still credible and reasonable (in the light of new criteria of credibility and new modes of reasoning).

Out of this questioning and critical discussion of ancient wisdom and long accepted religion arose what we call Greek philosophy, mathematics, natural science, political theory, indeed, many of the ways of thinking and discussion that shaped Western European culture.

What was probably the most important contribution of these classical students was the invention of habit breaking, as Gilbert Murray, the distinguished scholar and interpreter of Greek life and thought, has called it. By that he meant that the Greeks, probably for the first time in the history of mankind, developed a systematic practice of criticizing their traditional beliefs and patterns, their habits and institutions, and found, to their later dismay, that as they examined their traditions and questioned their customary beliefs and assumptions, their habitual ways of living, acting, feeling, of conducting their personal and group lives, they had undermined and eventually destroyed their customary social order.

In the succeeding centuries, the fourth and third especially, the process of disintegration and of demoralization was accelerated and Greek life lost its former order and reasonableness. But out of their earlier explorations and inventions they had developed two ideas which were later on in European history to play enormously significant roles—the idea of human potentialities with all that it implied for undiscovered possibilities of human achievement, and the idea of critical thinking with all its dynamics for social and cultural change.

Another period in our history was notable for the changes and the development of new patterns of thought and action and the rise of new sensibilities or feelings. This was the period we have learned to call the Renaissance—the period of so-called rebirth of Western European life. It has been studied and described by many scholars as a large movement which spread all over Western Europe and as a peculiarly oriented and differently focused development in each of the different areas of Europe, such as Italy, France, the Low Countries, and England. While there is still no general agreement upon what took place and how it arose, yet this period of great activity and bold thinking and action is recognized as having had profound consequences.

It is generally agreed that the new scientific knowledge, coming from Copernicus, Galileo, Kepler, and later Newton, called into question most of the accepted beliefs about the universe and how events happened which had been derived from early Greek and Egyptian thought and from the Judaic-Christian teachings which embodied these classical ideas and others from the Near East.

Scholars still are discussing and often disputing over the sources and the development of the Renaissance, how it developed, flowered in art and architecture, literature and music, and gave an impetus to voyages of discovery, bringing new ways of living, new ways of evaluating what was believed and what was done and not done.

It seems clear that one great stimulus to these developments was the rediscovery of the literature and arts of the past—especially of Greece. After centuries of preoccupation with the assumptions and beliefs of the Christian philosophers and theologians who interpreted all life in terms of rigid and very limited conceptions, Greek literature brought a new hope and a new orientation in the ideas and the daring speculation of classical Greece.

Central in these, and having the greatest influence apparently upon the men of the Renaissance, was the conception of human potentialities—that man could, and in the past actually did, think, act, feel, wonder and question in ways that were new and different from the customary patterns of so-called medieval thought; moreover, that man could live in different ways.

This conception of human potentialities which the Greek philosophers had developed and only partly explored was further enhanced by the other great contribution from Greek thinkers—of critical thinking and questioning traditions as expressed in art, architecture, literature, human relationships, law and social order.

Any attempted interpretation of the Renaissance is sure to be partial and distorted, because no one apparently can fully grasp this period of creative activity when almost every aspect of life was seen in a new light, was examined, often challenged, sometimes boldly discarded, and when even the most venerable beliefs and powerful organizations were subject to critical examination and alteration.

If we try to see this period in the light of our own contemporary problems and needs, we might say that Western European culture did undergo a new birth, in which much of the past was continued, but modified, changed, revised and reoriented, as the more intelligent and courageous men of that time responded to the new conceptions of nature and of man with new hope and higher aspirations, with new assumptions and new feelings about the universe in which they lived, and especially with new ideas about human nature.

Indeed, it might be said that in this period, man, Western European man, developed a new image of himself, with potentialities he had never dared previously to imagine. This new image of self, reinforced with the new ways of conceiving the universe, the operations of nature, the relationships among events, has been the central core of Western European culture and the source of dynamics for the past four or five centuries.

This, then, brings us to the contemporary world, not the familiar, small world of European life and thought, but to the entire world with all the millions and millions of people, each with their different cultures and social orders.

Today the whole world is entering upon a Renaissance as the traditional ideas and beliefs, the customary designs for living in each group of people, undergo progressive breakdown and dissolution.

As happened in Europe some centuries ago, every group of people is being exposed to new ideas, new assumptions, new tools and techniques (which are ideas put into practice). Thus, traditional religion, philosophy, law, morals and ethics, their customary beliefs about nature and man are becoming less and less credible, less and less acceptable and applicable.

We, the Western European group and the peoples of other lands and cultures, are all confronted with this impact of new knowledge and new understanding, of new insights and awarenesses, of new discoveries, inventions, techniques and machines. The initial impact as exhibited in Greece long ago, as in Europe for the past few centuries, or in England in the late eighteenth and early nineteenth centuries, produces dismay and anxiety. People are troubled and perplexed as they experience the loss of their older certainties, the passing of what they have long lived by and for. Their customary social order becomes less and less tolerable or unworkable as they are compelled to modify, to improvise, to discard and to learn new ways of living, of working, of carrying on their group activities and their human relations.

Everywhere people are facing much the same problems, and also the same conflicts, engendered by the resistance to change on the part of some and the eagerness to change on the part of others, one invoking traditions and the authority of long established teachings and organizations to oppose change, the others looking to the new concepts, the new techniques, the new practices as justifying and necessitating change.

Underneath these innumerable disputes, conflicts, problems, and the anxieties and aspirations they express, we are developing, as described in the following chapters, a new climate of opinion, with a new body of assumptions and conceptions about nature and about man coming from scientific studies, from scholarly investigations, from clinical insights, from artistic awarenesses, the critical and creative imagination of all those who, released from the coercion of traditions, are creating new patterns of thinking, new practices for working, new relationships for living, new images of man.

Today we are all so troubled and perplexed, so disturbed by the many events which far and near are threatening our security, that almost all of us are living without much awareness or understanding of what is going on around us. We are living the events which for centuries to come will be minutely studied by scholars who will undoubtedly describe these days as probably the most exciting and creative in the history of mankind. But, preoccupied with our daily chores, our worries and our personal hopes and ambitions, few of us are actually living in the present.

We are, for the most part, living fossils, shut within the narrow walls of our "private worlds" where these great changes and upheavals and these immense creative endeavors appear primarily as dangers to ourselves and threats to our customary ways of living. Outside in the actual world of events the dynamics of cultural and social change are operating, and we, whether we realize it or not, are participating if only by denying and resisting these changes for which many are devoting their lives. As in all social change, some groups are losing their former advantages and privileges and other groups are beginning to rise to more desirable status and a larger share of what is available.

One explanation for the apathy toward these exciting events, or this often frantic resistance to change, is the confusion and the acute conflicts over what is happening, what should happen and why. Everywhere there are strong and vehement individuals and groups advocating this or that change and equally strong and vehement groups opposing such changes and denouncing all those who favor change.

Thus, in almost every area there are conflicts which are hard to appraise and from which many shrink because they do not like these disputes and the open conflicts they sometimes lead to. What part each can and should play in these controversies will be interpreted differently by individuals, each with his or her traditional background, his or her personality. The loosening of former loyalties is bringing some surprising developments and unexpected exhibitions of individual and group repudiation of patriotic beliefs and loyalties.

It does seem clear that, underneath these disputes and these acute differences of opinion, these often conflicting responses to contemporary problems, there is a new climate of opinion

emerging, a new body of assumptions and a new way of thinking about nature and man which every intelligent individual
should try to understand.

Until recently we have conceived of man as outside of
nature, separate and distinct from the geographical environment and also from culture and social order. Having so
conceived of man and endowed him with special power and
un-natural capacities, we have set him off against nature and
society. Today we are developing an ecological approach, beginning to understand man in his environment, not only of
nature in and from which he evolved, but of culture and social
life which he has created for human living. Through transactions with nature man has developed what is essentially
human but which historically has been regarded as superhuman and supernatural.

Today we have new conceptions and new ways of thinking
of man and his environment, of how he has established his human way of living as a product of his human capacities.

These new conceptions are not yet fully defined and clari-
fied as they will be in the years to come, but already their
meaning, and especially their implications for today, for to-
morrow, are becoming evident. It is these conceptions, these
new and more fruitful ways of thinking which will increasingly
find expression in the social life and in the "private worlds" of
our children and of their children.

We cannot with much confidence predict "the shape of
things to come" nor clearly envisage what our descendants
will think and do, because most of us are still handicapped
by the older ideals and expectations, unable to conceive of the
future except in terms of an escape from or alleviation of our
present frustrations and unhappiness. As has been pointed out,
few of us could live in the kind of future social life for which
so many are striving because we have built a picture of that

future so largely in terms of preventing or abolishing something
or rejecting the institutions, the relationships and the practices
from which we now suffer.

But if we can begin to grasp these new conceptions of man
and of nature, if we can, fumblingly at first but with growing
confidence, try to think in the new ways, we can to some extent
realize what that future will involve, because that future life
is being initially shaped today by these emerging new ideas,
these new assumptions, and by the new and more hopeful expectations they are offering us.

Ideas are dynamic. A new idea, a new way of conceiving
events, operates to shift our focus, to give us an altered perspective. It makes us begin to see and think and act in different
ways, as Galileo changed our conception of motion and Copernicus changed our ideas of the universe. The new idea indicates
that what we have previously assumed and what we have accepted are no longer to be taken for granted. The shape, the
form, the meaning, the relationship in which we have perceived
events, are all altered, if only slightly, by the new conception.
This alteration or revision, however minor we may consider it,
modifies other perceptions and to some extent changes all the
ideas relevant to, or in any way connected with, the original
new idea, as Galileo's physics led to widespread revision of the
beliefs about nature.

Thus, we may say that a new idea disturbs the existing
stock of ideas and distorts the accepted frame of reference. In
our endeavor to restore the former coherence and balance, to
remedy the disturbing situation, we are compelled to examine
these other ideas and assumptions. Apparently it was this endeavor to reconcile Ptolemaic astronomy with Aristotelian ideas
that led Copernicus to develop the conceptions that began
modern astronomy.

Thus, what starts as a new idea, a novel conception in one

field of thought or area of living, gradually begins to permeate into others as the new idea dynamically operates in our thinking and actions to affect all the rest of our lives.

This is the process at work today, a process we have seen operating before and we can, therefore, begin to anticipate what it will produce in the way of a cumulative revision of our climate of opinion.

It was Emerson who asked, "If there is any period one would desire to be born in, is it not the age of Revolution? When the old and the new stand side by side and admit of being compared; when the energies of all men are searched by fear and hope; when the historic glories of the old can be compensated by the rich possibilities of the new era?"

Central to the future, as it is of crucial significance for today, is the conception of man, of human nature, the potentialities of the human organism. Like the men of the Renaissance, we can today project forward and begin to discuss and plan in terms of this new image of man and the possibility of believing in human beings.

Today for the first time we are realizing what we mean, or can mean, by the belief in the value and worth of the human personality, what are the full implications of the dignity of man as seen in the light of our present day conception of man in nature and nature in man. The eighteenth century poets expressed this conception of man in nature, but today we are more prepared to accept such an idea and its correlative that nature is in man, which is perhaps less clearly understood.

Today we are starting a new tradition, a tradition about traditions, realizing that it is not the specific content or beliefs or form or pattern, but the aspirations that gave rise to those historical beliefs and institutions or ways of living, which are the central core of tradition. From these aspirations we may derive the courage and inspiration to carry on. In other words, we are loyal to our traditions and can maintain the values we cherish only by recognizing that the beliefs and practices, the historically developed institutions and patterns of human relations are all efforts to attain these goals. In the light of new understanding, the only way we can maintain tradition, can carry on the endless striving for our values, is by changing our beliefs and institutions.

More specifically, we are today not only privileged but obligated by our traditions to re-examine the ideas we have long accepted about nature and about man, the relations of man to nature and of nature to man.

For this purpose we may fruitfully conceive of man living in an environment with many dimensions. This multi-dimensional environment is not to be viewed as a series of concurrent but separate environments: it is to be approached as an environment which has many potentialities, of which man is one product, and of which human culture and social order and personality are also products, notable as man's own creation within that all-embracing environment. Thus we can conceive of a totality of nature in which we may distinguish man as a unique participant in the organism-environment complex we are striving to understand.

This way of thinking helps us to avoid the common practice of fractionating the field of nature-man into seemingly separate, discrete portions, each of which is then further analyzed into factors, agents and parts, with various assumed modes of operation peculiar to each portion or agent.

Instead, we may approach this multi-dimensional environment as a total field in which we may observe the processes common to all these supposedly separate portions operating to produce different products depending upon when and how and what they operate upon.

It would be absurd and grossly misleading to assert or even to imply that we can today achieve such a task as is here being attempted. There are inevitably many errors and misinterpretations in the pages that follow, since no one person can pretend to grasp all the new knowledge and new conceptions. Moreover, we can be sure that what is today accepted as valid will be more or less altered, revised, even superseded in the future as we go on exploring, critically examining, developing new insights and understandings. At best, therefore, we can only tentatively formulate and experimentally apply these new conceptions and the new ways of thinking they now make possible, as set forth in the several chapters which discuss different dimensions of the nature-man field.

Specifically the reader will find in the following chapters an interpretation of the new conceptions of the universe and more especially of the geographical environment we call nature, as we are learning to understand it in dynamic terms.

Then he will see in the next chapter a discussion of the man's internal environment viewed as an expression of the basic processes operating in the geographical environment and as the core of man's image of the self.

Following this is an exposition of the cultural environments which each group of people has developed as their design for living, by selective awareness and meaningful interpretation of the geographical and the internal environments.

The succeeding chapter on the social environment shows how each group of people has established a social order with its patterns of conduct and its symbols and rituals to regulate their group life and human relations.

The chapter on our "private worlds" carries this a step further by revealing how each member of the group lives, as if in a "private world" of his own, created and maintained by the dynamic processes we call personality.

In the final chapter there is an over-all interpretation of the larger meaning and profound implications of these new ways of conceiving nature and man, which give promise of replacing our now archaic beliefs with new dynamic assumptions we can live by and for.

II

The Geographical Environment

We HUMANS LIKE TO THINK of ourselves as the most important of all organisms, as the stars in the play, with the geographical environment and all the plants and animals therein as scenery and props for our human drama, if and when we do think of them. But this self-centered view of nature and ourselves, while often comforting, is both misleading and obstructive.

We should try to think of ourselves as one of many organisms on this vast stage of nature, where we must recognize that we play only one part in this ongoing drama of existence. Usually we are a disturbing, often a destructive, agency, but like other organisms, we are involved in the complicated interrelationships and we actively participate in and help to maintain the totality we call nature. Indeed, we should think of our-selves as being used by other organisms and natural processes, one of the many configurations of energy that make up the totality of existence, partaking in and being carried along by these larger equilibrating and compensation processes of nature.

To think of man in this way may be painful to our pride and even disturbing to our usual complacent self-assurance. But if we want to gain a better understanding of man's place in nature and his multi-dimensional environment, we should try to achieve this detachment and see ourselves in this larger setting. Thereby we can attain a larger and deeper space-time perspective.

Thus, we can begin to think of the immense universe in which our green mantled earth is but a tiny speck whirling around our sun, one of the many stars that range throughout space-time. Our earth is part of this larger complex, resonating to the cosmic events and processes to which it is continually exposed, participating in this self-regulating, self-equilibrating universe which we are beginning to understand as a dynamic field.

On our familiar earth, mighty processes are at work, never ceasing in their operation, as we will realize when we recall what is going on around us.

The world we live in that we call nature is an ongoing series of events and continuously active processes, physical, chemical and biological. These same basic circular processes of our earth are operating in the farthest stars modified by the stellar temperatures and pressures and their occurrence in that remote space-time. Everything that exists and happens in the world—on land or sea, in the depths of the earth or in the air—we are beginning to understand in terms of these regular, re-current, almost uniform processes and events.

The totality of events we call the universe is being revealed as a dynamic organized whole or field, a series of interrelated energy transformations giving rise to what we call physical, chemical and biological processes and the innumerable products they generate. The sun, according to recent studies, operates by a continuous circular process of transformations that are not dissimilar to those operating here on our earth, but with greater intensity.

It is important to realize clearly what a process involves. A process can never be observed directly; it can be inferred from its products and its relationships to other processes. It is a dynamic operation which can occur in a wide variety of locations and can utilize a wide variety of substances with which to produce sometimes different but basically similar or equivalent products. Thus, fire is a process that can be generated in many different ways—rubbing two sticks together, focusing the sun's rays with a lens, striking a match, combining two chemicals, short-circuiting an electrical power line or otherwise raising the temperature until fire starts. And this fire process, of chemical transformation by combining with oxygen, can utilize a wide variety of substances, such as wood, fiber, coal, oil, various chemicals, for such combustion, to produce a different kind of ash according to the fuel substances consumed.

Fertilization and gestation are biological processes of development and growth, producing a new organism or seed. While the process is basically alike in each species of plant or animal, the products are different according to the plant or animal in which they occur. Thus, the same process of plant fertilization produces strawberries or hickory nuts, of animal fertilization produces kittens, puppies, elephants, whales or human infants.

We may say that the underlying processes of nature are basically similar, but operating in different settings, in different complexes, upon different substances, at different rates, they produce the great diversity of plants and animals, of climate and weather and the other characteristics of different geographical locations.

To grasp the meaning of the world we live in, viewed as a dynamic complex of active processes, we must try to realize how the great variety of products—plants, animals, human beings, land and water, mountains and plains, desert and jungle, rocks and minerals, liquids, solids and gases—are all produced by the same basic processes we call physical, chemical and biological.

At the level of subatomic processes we are discovering what an immense amount of energy operates "inside the atom"; how the different electrical changes are ceaselessly interacting to maintain the atom, occasionally, as in radioactive elements like radium and uranium, emitting an electrical impulse.

Then too we must try to visualize atoms clustering together with tight bonds to form molecules of like atoms or of unlike atoms. These molecules are patterned configurations within which each atom occupies its specific location. Most of the activities we call chemical—such as combustion of molecules (slowly as in rusting or quickly as in flame) the biological processes of digestion, assimilation, of repair and resistance—are molecular interactions, sometimes in minute organisms.

In a gas it has been shown that apparently there are innumerable molecules moving at random, at different rates and distances, reacting with other moving molecules. These random, disorderly motions are so numerous and frequent they give rise to a statistical order, in that certain average frequencies persistently recur and converge into regularities which we call volume, pressure, temperature, etc., so long as the gas is enclosed in a container of some kind and has boundaries. Without boundaries the gas diffuses and loses its "order." This order arising from disorder was the great discovery of physical science which, with the aid of mathematics, has made possible the science of mechanics and the practice of engineering, all predicated upon these recurrent regularities produced by large scale, disorderly events converging into what we call cause and effect relations.

Molecules as aggregations of atoms occur not only in the highly flexible state called a gas, but also in the liquid state, where again they exhibit ceaseless, disorderly activity which also shows order and recurrent regularities as the great frequency of such activities averages out and converges into the persistent fluid or liquid forms of behavior that we can predict and utilize practically, as in hydraulics, or in what are called colloids that appear as gels or sols, behaving sometimes as a liquid and sometimes as a solid.

Molecules also become aggregated into the solid state where their range of motion is more limited than in the liquid or the gas states and hence they exhibit, again by persistent frequencies, the characteristics we associate with solids, such as stable dimensions, density, hardness, etc.

These molecules are actively engaged in maintaining the relatively fixed size, shape and other characteristics of solids; the atoms making up each molecule are also energetically operating to maintain the molecule, while within the atom there is intense activity and enormous energies not revealed or released except insofar as the behavior of the atom exhibits this internal activity.

Some solid aggregates are relatively fixed and unchanging, altering very slowly, like crystals and rocks, especially those which are not exposed to air, water or other activities. Other molecular aggregates are not fixed and unchanging, but exhibit a greater or less degree of persistent size, shape and activity level, persisting by a process of continual transactions, not only among the molecules, but with the environing world.

Thus organisms like plants and animals grow, develop, mature and continually function as living organisms through a ceaseless process of taking in and releasing molecules of the environment. Some of these, broken down into various constituent atoms, are incorporated into the living, growing body, replacing other atoms in molecules, often of the same chemical substance, such as the ceaseless intake of calcium atoms and replacement of other calcium atoms in bones and teeth.

The larger aggregates of molecules called organisms are like the molecules which persist through ceaseless activity of their constituent atoms or the atoms which persist through ceaseless activity of their constituent electrical impulses or charges.

Here we see how on different levels of complexity, of homogeneity and heterogeneity, the same principle operates. Each larger aggregate is constituted of individuals, each of which has a specific location in the larger pattern; this is actively engaged in the behavior that makes possible the rise and persistence of that larger aggregate which in turn bounds, patterns and otherwise governs its constituents.

But there is observable a highly significant difference in these processes. In physical and chemical substances and processes there is a statistical order and regularity among the innumerable anonymous and highly random, disorderly "parts" or events. The multiplicity of these random events generates recurrent frequencies which are orderly, predictable and dependable so that regularities or patterns appear when these activities are bounded. Without boundaries and limits the gas, the liquid and the solid rapidly or slowly breaks down, loses energy, diffuses, evaporates, disintegrates. Entropy operates and disorder replaces order.

In living organisms and probably in some of the in-between organizations, like slime molds and viruses, there are patterns or organizations which arise, not from disorder, but from the order and the recurrent regularities of other organisms that produce these offspring or descendants. The organism persists by continually changing and reproducing itself, giving a pattern to its offspring for that offspring's existence.

Over the millions and millions of years of organic evolution, order, pattern, organization have developed as persistent shapes, forms, configurations, which we call organisms that are produced by other organisms and so exhibit, as they grow and develop or divide and multiply, the patterns of activity that are characteristic of each kind of organism but with variations in size, shape and functional efficiency and age.

The human organism is a product of that evolutionary process wherein these persistent configurations became established and transmittable through eggs and sperms in which this organizing function is passed on to the offspring to operate in its growth and development and its functioning activities.

In living organisms we see then this other kind of order and regularity which is exhibited, not in recurrent frequencies as in a gas or stable dimensions as in a rock, but in configurations that grow and change and persist by repeatedly altering their dimensions and by continually replacing their constituents and thereby postponing disorder until death. Thus order of a patterned, organized nature is maintained in the midst of the seeming disorder of the environment, by a continual intake and expenditure of energy in circular dynamic processes, to keep that patterned organic configuration operating.

The operation of a circular process in a field becomes more understandable when we remember that such a process is dynamic and operates more or less continuously. Thus when we say the "parts" create and maintain the "whole" which reciprocally governs the activities of those "parts," it should be recognized that some of the "parts" are active earlier than others so that in this circular process the "parts" are engaged in different phases of the circular, or cyclical, process as in an autocatalytic reaction. It is this repetition and timing of activities that give significant clues to the total circular process and the meaning of a field as to the space-time configuration in which such circular processes are dynamically operating.

This circular operation is also to be observed in social order and culture, as will be pointed out later, where the adults who are maintaining social order and the cultural environment by their learned activities are engaged in patterning the activities of their children who will grow up to continue the process. Thus the adults maintain the social-cultural field which reciprocally governs their activities and guides them as parents to rear their children to do likewise.

This appears to be the way living processes operate as cells, tissues, fluids engage in these circular operations into which new cells, tissues and fluids are continually entering to carry on the continuous processes of living and to maintain the organism-field in which all these activities are interrelated and governed by the total organic field that they thus maintain.

The aggregate of organisms which make the plants and animals of the world again are constellated in life zones where they maintain what we call the environment which persists so long as the "balance of nature," the innumerable transactions of plant and animal organisms, continue within certain limits of fluctuation. When these limits are exceeded and one species of plants or of animals grows too frequent or too scarce, the environment reaches a climax and begins to alter cumulatively and often irreversibly and all the organisms therein are compelled to alter their ways of living and of utilizing the changing environment. Thus these changes are cumulative as in all circular processes.

Our geographical environment, therefore, is the space-time setting of man's existence and man, himself, is one of the products of those natural processes which have produced so many other organisms, plant and animal and some in-between, like the slime molds or virus, all operating with much the same basic processes.

We must pause and reflect a bit to grasp the amazing complexity of life patterns that exist around us. If we go out into the open, to a partially wooded area with a stream or pond, and begin to explore, we will find a host of different organisms all existing within the same limited geographical environment.

There will be an extraordinary number and variety of plant and animal life, from the simplest organisms like the bacteria in the soil and the molds and mosses, on through a series of growing complexities, worms, insects, bugs, butterflies and moths, frogs, snakes and other reptiles, fish, crustaceans and other organisms living in the water, birds and bats and other small mammals, like moles, squirrels and mice, larger mammals like rabbits, fox and deer, the domesticated animals, dogs, cows, sheep, and man.

What is important to realize is that each of these organisms lives in the same geographical environment, selectively utilizing the same basic processes for its existence and survival and yet each maintains its own specialized, organic structure-functions and individualized ways of life in that environment.

By artificial breeding and by radiation man has evoked new and unsuspected potentialities in many organisms, plant and animal, producing new strains and variations. Stability of a species apparently arises from resistance to change or lack of exposure to events that can provoke variations, which indicates that each species has developed a selective awareness and limited responsiveness to the environment, perhaps through a capacity to equalize the fluctuations in the environment. Thus a species can go on maintaining its specific design for living in the same environment with organisms of very different kinds, each with its different design for living in that same environment.

The geographical environment of nature has offered innumerable possibilities to the many different organisms, each of which has learned selectively to utilize that environment for what it needs for its continued existence.

Evolution and what we have called "natural selection"

has been a process of organism-environmental transactions, wherein sometimes the organism has adapted to the environment and sometimes the organism has developed new capacities —structural, functional, behavioral—to maintain itself by more effective use of the potentialities of the environment. New organisms have arisen with altered selective awareness and new capacities for evoking and utilizing the environmental potentialities, thereby modifying the environment and contributing to its evolution.

Most organisms have a fixed, almost unchangeable, way of living, in a well-defined environmental setting, a life zone from which they cannot ordinarily escape or, if they do, cannot long surivive. Long ago each kind of organism evolved and developed the more or less specialized structures and functions and activities upon which they are dependent for survival. The earth is filled with the fossil remains of long extinct species which lived and flourished in remote ages and then died out, apparently because their specialized way of life could not change to meet the alterations in their environment, like the dinosaurs who ruled the earth in the Age of Reptiles. Likewise, there were many plant forms, resembling the tree ferns, which are now extinct.

Some organisms have survived by minimizing their requirements or by developing strong defenses. There are sea organisms, like the molluscs, which live in their hard shells as they did millions of years ago, and there are molds of ancient days still flourishing, like pencillium, from which we now derive potent substances for fighting disease germs. It is interesting to speculate that perhaps this capacity to kill or stop the growth of germs evolved long ago when the only organisms on land were these lowly molds and the bacteria and bacillus of what we now call disease germs.

The geographical environment is versatile; these basic, physical, chemical and biological processes have produced not only these diverse plant and animal organisms but also furnished the equally diversified food sustenance for their survival. Out of these many forms of living organisms, with their amazing designs for living, each deriving from the same environment, have arisen many diverse and highly complicated interrelationships.

Being more or less restricted to a prescribed geographical location, where the necessary conditions of life are available—temperature, moisture or aridity, light or darkness, and other climatic conditions—each organism has a more or less fixed life zone, its customary area or range of living. Within that life zone it has its established way of gaining food and defending itself by force or by strategy.

Thus most animal organisms are predators—they live by killing other organisms for food, which is the practice of all organisms to a greater or less extent. Some exist by killing and eating only plant organisms, but the true predators kill and eat other animal organisms, like the big cats, the lion and tiger, or the small but fierce shrew, and, of course, man who likewise lives by slaughtering animals for food and also eating plant products.

While different organisms may eat the same food, such as cows, chickens, pigs, sheep, which eat corn, oats, etc., each converts these same nutrients into its own specific cells, tissues, body forms and covering such as hide, feathers, wool, etc. This is another illustration of the way in which the same process of digestion, assimilation, metabolism, may produce different products when operating in different fields and upon different, but equivalent, constituents.

It is interesting to note that each organism has its more or less specialized food requirements, depending in part upon what it cannot produce within its own organism. Thus the need of vitamins, for example, differs among plants and animals. Man, like monkeys and the guinea pig, needs vitamin C in his food because he cannot produce it himself as do other animals.

Some organisms enter into a sort of partnership arrangement of mutual aid, called symbiosis, receiving what each needs from the other, in a reciprocal arrangement. Others are parasitic, wholly dependent upon a host plant, like orchids, or mistletoe, or animals like body lice or ticks, or malaria and other internal parasites. Some of these parasites are friendly and helpful, like the organisms that live in the digestive tract and help to digest the animal's food; others are malignant and destructive, like malaria and various worms which live in animals.

Then there are the virus organisms, difficult to define precisely because so elusive. They can live, apparently, only within living organic cells where they behave like parasitic organisms, yet they can be dried, crystallized and then restored to living activity.

The number and variety of these interrelations are amazing in their diversity and complexity. Each organism lives by its selective capacity for utilizing the environment to provide what it requires for its eixstence and its perpetuation. There are, for example, very simple plant organisms, like the algae, which live in the boiling hot water of the Yellowstone geysers; fish that live in abysmal depths of the ocean under such tremendous pressure that they blow up when brought to the surface of the sea.

We can begin to think of these plant and animal organisms and the in-betweens as different constellations or configurations, engaged in the capture, storage and release of energy from their environment to which it returns in altered forms, partially during the organism's life in the form of excretions, including the air it breathes out, and wholly when the organism dies and rapidly or slowly disintegrates into its constituent chemical substances. Each takes from the common public world of nature what it needs and likewise responds to the requirements of that environment in its own specialized way.

The organic life cycle is maintained by these energy transformations which occur through the basic physical, chemical and biological processes which within each organism operate to produce the diversified products necessary for the organism's complicated living processes, including reproduction.

Through millions of years of experimentation, with a variety of different forms and structures and combinations of functions, many of which did not long survive, there has evolved what is called the web of nature—the balance of nature—a dynamic, ever-changing equilibrium, around which plants and animals fluctuate, as they interact in varying quantities, increasing or decreasing in rhythmic or irregular cycles.

Here we see a more or less systematic arrangement—a complex of regular, recurrent, self-equilibrating interrelationships occurring in the geographical environment which supplies both the disturbing and the balancing processes, as the environment in turn responds to the larger disturbances to which it is subject.

It is evident that the long accepted concept of organisms *and* environment, as if the organism were a tenant in a large room, needs to be revised, to recognize the circular, dynamic interrelations of organisms-environment. Organisms, plant and animal, make up the environment in which they live by selective awareness and response to and making use of the other organisms and the ongoing physical, chemical and other biological processes that are operating in the geographical environment.

Thus the environment likewise uses the organisms to maintain itself (and to evolve) as much as the organisms use the environment. Each organism selectively takes from and returns to the common geographical environment according to its role in that life zone. What one takes and incorporates into its organism becomes the food for another which returns as urine or faeces what will nourish that food, as we see in the familiar pasture-cattle cycle. What one organism does to the geographical environment, like the bacteria which break down or release substances which are essential to the life processes of other organisms, illustrates this circular process.

Over varying periods of years this web of nature, this fluctuating balance, is maintained by innumerable interactions and adjustments, effective in restoring the disturbed equilibrium, or in slowly shifting to another balance. The continuity of nature arises from the short-term life cycles of organisms and cyclical seasonal recurrences.

"I play for Seasons; not Eternities," says Nature. . . .
*Pledged she herself to aught, 't would mark her end.**

The earth is still laboring to maintain its equilibrium, as we are reminded by the innumerable earthquakes of greater or lesser intensity and extent, as the great masses of the earth's crust move and shift in a never ending series of internal readjustments. Some areas of the earth's crust are more stabilized than others today, but the geological record shows that in ages past all the land and seas were repeatedly altered while great mountain ranges rose from the earth's surface, towered high for a period, and then were lowered or eroded down. The seas covered large areas and then retreated, leaving land areas which again were submerged ages later.

These large movements, horizontal and vertical, are the outward expression of the equilibrating processes at work in the earth's crust, just as the volcanoes and geysers which periodically erupt or the boiling springs that flow to the surface

* George Meredith, *Modern Love*, XIII.

— *28* —

give evidence of the tremendous pressures and heat within the earth which break forth from time to time and reach the earth's surface. The dynamics of environment arise from those highly diverse configurations which make up the environmental field and by their interrelated processes give rise to the fluctuations, disturbances and compensatory changes that maintain the earth.

On the earth's surface, wind and rain, snow and ice, fluctuating with the impact of the sun's heat, are operating daily to break down the earth's surface, slowly crumbling the high mountains and gouging out deep valleys and gorges in the plains. Season after season, year after year, the ceaseless processes of gradation and erosion are taking place, breaking down into ever smaller particles to produce sand or clay which, mixed with decaying vegetation, becomes soil.

What is happening today has been happening for ages, during which profound alterations of the earth's surface have occurred, only later producing the soil in which plant and animal life could arise.

The rains and the melting ice from glaciers and smaller mountain streams are coursing toward the sea, some like the mighty Mississippi, or Amazon, carrying down immense loads of silt and soil. Every time there is a flood, a greater or less portion of the earth's surface is carried away, resulting, as we see, in the ever-widening and deepening gulleys or eroded land and the blocked up river deltas.

These impacts upon the earth's surface are in turn the products of the stupendous processes of our changing atmosphere, the ever-changing weather, which reflects the shifting air masses, of hot and cold and moisture-laden air, which rise and fall or swirl in ever-widening circles that we experience as storms, hurricanes and typhoons. The winds sweep the earth, bringing rains and storms to some areas and droughts to others, which directly modify the local geographical environment of plants and animals, each of which is affected to a greater or less extent by these events. The long-term changes in weather or climate probably reflect alterations in the sun's output or in what the earth receives from the sun.

These ever-changing air masses, with their continual alterations in pressures and disturbances, including the electrical storms of often violent intensity, are part of the dynamics of a world that maintains itself relatively stable and enduring by these ceaseless processes. Nothing is static or fixed in or on the earth because everything is essentially energy in various complexes that interact and by these interactions and transactions maintain what we call existence. Nothing is fixed and static; since existence is activity and lack of activity would mean the end of energy and finality. There is no "inert matter" as we once believed. Everything that exists and every event arise from the continuous dynamic processes which maintain the visible, tangible size, shape and other properties of "things" and sustain the operations called events.

Indeed, the whole universe is being revealed as a dynamic constellation which, like Alice in Wonderland, runs with incredible speed in order to stand (apparently) still.

Thus, we can look at our little earth, which travels in its more or less fixed orbit around the sun (if we take the sun as the point of reference to describe the earth's motions), moving through space-time at incredible speed, turning daily upon its axis and exposing first one surface toward the sun and then another, to bring the seasonal changes we call winter, spring, summer and autumn in the areas away from the equator.

Once we were told that this movement of the earth and of its sister planets around the sun was "caused" by the "force of gravitation" and we pictured the earth like a ball being swung around a huge elliptical circle at the end of a gigantic tether. Today we are trying to replace that familiar idea of a specific cause or force with a new conception, of space-time, of the way space and time are arranged and curved, so that we can view the earth's path around the sun as the only path it can pursue as it moves. The movements of the planets are not "caused" by special forces but are the paths through space-time which is warped and bent or curved, with varying density of localized matter-energy.

And the sun, upon whose bounty of energy, of heat and light, we are dependent, also moves along its path in curved space-time, along with the other neighboring stars in our galaxy which over long periods of time also appears to be shifting its seemingly fixed location.

Thus, we see a series of orderly changes and cyclic movements, of varying periods and rhythms, which we can begin to understand in terms of space-time and processes arising from fundamental energy transformations.

This viewpoint is bringing a significant alteration in our conception of the universe and giving us a new cosmic outlook. We are learning to live in a universe that operates, not by specific "causes" and "forces" or self-acting agents controlling each event (as earlier we tried to explain what happened). Rather, we can view whatever exists and happens as occurring within a space-time continuum, with energy transformations, that we call events. We can think of something more fundamental than forces or causes, which if we wish to use such terms, designate the local and observable manifestations of the basic processes of existence.

Thus, we are led to reformulate our ideas of the universe, our conception of events. We can view whatever happens as a process which we can describe as physical, chemical, geological, biological or by any other of the many specialized scientific names we give to different kinds of processes and products.

These processes arise from the dynamics of an ever-changing space-time in which certain configurations or energy complexes appear to be more stable than others, persisting seemingly unchanged while others are less stable and so are continually changing, absorbing, or giving off energy. The universe goes on, like a man riding a bicycle who has to keep pedalling or he will fall off. It calls for a new way of thinking to realize that even the most stable and enduring rocks continue to exist only by a continuous dynamic process which maintains their internal structural configuration.

Recently it has been shown that events are of two major classes. There are *convergent* events, where enormous numbers of more or less similar but anonymous events converge to give certain regularities and order, like the molecules in a gas; and there are *divergent* events, where one single identifiable event initiates a series of events, like the emission of an energy quantum which individually is a dynamic, unpredictable occurrence.

Classical physics gave us an understanding of convergent events by revealing the statistical order and regularity arising from a multitude of disorderly events. Quantum, atomic or nuclear physics is disclosing the operation of divergent events by studying the organization within the atom and the orderly patterned emission and absorption of individual energy quanta as they occur in a field.

Thus we can say that the universe exists and maintains itself by a dynamic process that we have localized as occurring "within the atoms," which today are conceived as composed of electrical charges, positive and negative and in-between, by their movement and interactions giving rise to the familiar forms of energy releases. There is apparently an unbroken spectrum of these energy transformations, observable waves or discrete radiations, ranging from the shortest and most intense, such as X-rays and the emanations from radium, through the different bands we call light, heat and radio.

Recently we have discovered how to start a process of fission within the atom, releasing immense energies hitherto not accessible. In this atomic fission we have apparently duplicated, on a small scale, a process similar to that operating in the sun to release the immense energy, of which only a small fraction reaches our earth in the form of sunlight and perhaps other rays.

We have also become aware of what we call cosmic rays that reach the earth apparently from outer space with great energy, although in exceedingly small quantities. Thus more and more we are discovering how we are exposed to a variety of impacts from the sun and perhaps from interstellar space, only some of which penetrate our atmosphere. Recently we have been able to explore beyond the earth's atmosphere with radar and rockets, thus revealing the many forms of energy transformation from which we are partially or wholly shielded by the earth's atmosphere.

Thus if we reflect upon the kind of universe we live in, as now conceived, we will see that the sun and other stars and planets, the rocks, land, water and oceans, climate or weather, plant and animal organisms, all exist as different configurations of energy which continue to exist or persist only by a ceaseless process, by actively absorbing and releasing or transforming energy. The sun gives out incredible amounts of energy, freely dispersed into space, some small portion of which, penetrating our atmosphere, reaches the earth and enters into the many terrestrial and organic processes that make up the earth and all its multitudinous activities.

In each organism, plant or animal or in-between, in each configuration or complex, there is a never ceasing activity within the atoms making up the substances of which it is composed, within and among the molecules, the cells, the crystals, the colloids, the liquids, gases and solids. Indeed, all is activity, the continuous process of energy interchange and transformation, producing all that exists.

Recent studies with isotopes, like heavy hydrogen (which is another less frequent form of hydrogen), and with tagged atoms, like phosphorus (which has been made radioactive by a cyclotron or by nuclear fission and so can be identified later and measured, in very small quantities), have made possible experimental studies of how organic processes in plants and animals take place—of how they selectively take in, retain or release these various chemical substances.

Thus it is becoming clear that organisms develop, grow in size and shape, mature and age, maintaining their identity as organisms (which can be followed individually) by this same process of ceaseless interchange. Each organism takes in air and utilizes some of its constituents for temporary or more enduring purposes, some using oxygen, some carbon dioxide, or other gases. Likewise, an organism may take in a variety of substances, circulate and assimilate the molecules and atoms into its organism wherein each organ system or cell will select out what it requires for its functioning. The apparently hard and enduring teeth or skeleton have been shown to be continuously taking in new atoms of calcium and phosphorus to replace those which have been released.

Apparently this same process of selective capture, storage and release of various chemical substances is going on in all living organisms, plant or animal, with greater or less intensity and rapidity of interchange, of accumulation and of disposal.

The conception of an organism, including man himself, is of a more or less persistent configuration, a slowly altering pattern through the years, through which the universe is ebbing and flowing, as daily it captures, stores and releases parts of the geographical environment. What is to be emphasized is that the organism persists through these continual changes; when it can no longer maintain these vital transactions, it dies and sooner or later disintegrates.

If we could, as suggested earlier, escape from our self-centered idea of ourselves as the star in this cosmic drama, we would see that man, the whole human race, like other organisms, is an inextricable part of this ongoing, never ceasing process of change, in which man is being used, if we may say so, just as all other organisms are being utilized, to keep the show going.

All other organisms, plant and animal and man, participate in the total organism-environmental process, and while man has learned to use the environment more effectively for his own purposes, he also is being used by the environment. Thus we should try to realize that man is continuously responding to the changing demands of the environment, of changing weather, hot and cold, humidity, barometric pressure, the impact of infections and insects, of parasites and other organisms. In his response to these changes, these demands and assaults, he maintains his own internal environment more or less steady. In doing this he also helps maintain the environment, often radically altering it by his practices of agriculture, animal husbandry, forestry, etc.

It may stretch our minds to think of man being "used by nature," but it is a necessary and more or less obvious corollary of man's using the environment, just as the plant life is used by nature to maintain the environment which the plants use for living and propagating. The circular, reciprocal, living, dynamic processes of nature are carried on by all organisms including man.

We like to speak of man's ability to "control nature," but this means that as man learns through scientific study to understand the order and processes of nature, he must increasingly "obey nature," that is, he must think and act in accordance with natural processes. He can control nature and get what he wants only by learning to think, act and work according to the requirements of nature.

We should realize that each individual is a temporary possessor of chemical substances which have for millions of years been utilized by all his predecessors in the long procession of organic forms through the ages. The air we breathe has been repeatedly used by other organisms, indeed, some of the vital oxygen we are so dependent upon has probably been only recently released by some plant organism. Much of what we eat is derived from plants and animals whose bodies contain the various elements needed by our organism to live and grow. Moreover, many of those elements were once part of organisms that lived ages ago. The atoms of calcium and phosphorus in our teeth may once have been the skeletons of minute sea organisms, or molluscs like clams and oysters; the iron atoms in our blood were probably once the major constituent of the innumerable bacteria which lived and died millions of years ago, each leaving behind a tiny store of iron it had captured from the environing water. Indeed, every part of us, including the constituents of those extraordinary, wholly unique cells in our brain that make possible our speaking, writing and utilization of symbols and the scientific study of these processes, have probably all been at different times incorporated in other organisms, plant or animal.

However otherwise we conceive of man, we are a product of and an inescapable contributor to the geographical environment in and through which we exist as organisms. We are, as it were, temporary concentrations of substances and of energy transformations, taken out of the environment by the selective processes of our organic functions, and we maintain this concentration in its changing form throughout the years of our life by carrying on this ceaseless intercourse with the environment. Indeed, we may say that the geographical environment of nature has, as it were, concentrated and organized some of its most dynamic and subtle processes into this complicated configuration we call man, just as it has concentrated and organized the innumerable other living organisms that make up the plants and animals and in-between organisms.

We exist in the geographical environment, moving about in space-time, as we carry on our continual intercourse with nature, through breathing, drinking, eating, absorbing light, heat and other forms of radiant energy, eliminating through breathing, urination and defecation, through the skin and by radiation of heat, as the geographical environment flows in and out of us, as it does in all other organisms. Thus, the long-accepted idea that man knows the world only through his senses expresses the old intellectual conception of human knowledge by a knower who was separate and apart from nature. Man's organic functional transactions with the environment are the basic relations with nature, further extended, sharpened and refined by sensory processes and by the human capacity to put meanings into all situations and deal with the environment in terms of symbols. Man "knows" the world in many ways of which his sensations and his conceptions are but a part of his continual transactions with nature.

Thus we can gain a new conception of nature and man, with man no longer outside, separate and aloof, as once was believed when we thought man was superior and outside nature. Man, we now see, is a part of nature, a product of the same amazing processes that have produced all the rest of nature, sharing in the same simplicity and orderliness and the same complexity of interrelated processes.

Man, seen in this perspective and identified with nature, gains a new and wondrous place in the world, gaining in dignity and worth, from sharing these mighty cosmic processes. He no longer needs to console himself and bolster up his pride with the older beliefs in his unique creation, since no story of man's special creation or supernatural endowment can begin to equal the full significance of his evolution in this geographical environment. Nor can any assumption of man's uniqueness based on his supposedly un-natural or supernatural capacities and potentialities, measure up to what we are now beginning to discover about this dynamic universe in which man has evolved as the latest expression of the apparently unlimited potentialities and the subtle plasticity of nature.

The earth, however small and insignificant it may appear in the finite, but unbounded, universe of curved space-time, is nevertheless essential to the cosmic processes, playing its part in the total dynamic field. The universe, as we can now conceive it, including our earth and all it embraces, is not an aimlessly drifting, unguided "materialistic" existence. It is a beautifully ordered complex, interrelated to the farthest reaches of space-time, wherein everything that happens, each event is both spontaneous, to a greater or less degree, and also sequentially related to what has happened before and what will happen after, always responsive to the larger field it helps to create and maintain.

This newly revealed universe is not the mechanically conceived model of fixed, unvarying action of the nineteenth century cosmologies wherein everything was precisely determined and fixed, wherein nature had rigid, unchanging boundaries and unvarying patterns, because everything was believed to be run by mechanical forces. We can no longer complacently assume that scientific research will be able to predict everything that happens, bringing all activities within a few mathematical formulas.

We have inherited a traditional conception of the universe, organized and operated on a dominance-submission basis, by some power or authority which exercises control over submissive, passive particles, organisms, human beings. We have a traditional idea of a world created by fiat of an omnipotent deity who has ruled the universe according to his dictates and his feelings, often disturbing the orderly process of events to favor man or to punish him.

All our historical conceptions, of nature and of social life, were built upon this same basic pattern of some power, force, cause or authority which controlled and directed whatever happened, told man what he could and could not do, speaking as deity, king, emperor, or as boss. Organization, therefore, was conceived as a collection of parts or persons which some mysterious power or force or authority, as in the church, state, the military, kept together and compelled to operate with greater or less interrelatedness.

Today we have a new conception of the universe as self-governed and self-regulating, interrelated and interacting to the farthest reach of space-time. Moreover we can view the universe in a new space-time perspective. Instead of the relatively restricted universe of our traditional conception, limited to the earth and the sun with its other planets, we now can view the universe as unbounded, with space-time extending out and beyond any of the boundaries we once thought fixed. The universe, as now conceived, is finite but unbounded, with curved space-time, in and through which each particle, each atom and electron traverses its world lines.

Moreover, we now view the universe in a new time perspective, in which the earth has an immensely extended age, going back millions and millions of years with a future of almost unlimited duration. This new time perspective changes the familiar dimension of our existence and calls for a reformulation of our values and aspirations, as we recognize human existence in this larger framework. No longer will the older provisional ethics of our traditions suffice since the new time perspective calls for long-term ethics, conceived in terms of man's ongoing development as an organism and as a human being with a culture and social order and an immense future ahead.

It calls for a radical alteration in all our customary ideas and patterns of thinking to grasp these new conceptions and to think in terms of these new spatial and time perspectives. It is especially difficult for us to escape from the older assumption of everything's being controlled or regulated by some mysterious power or force or divine fiat. Thus we must make an effort to achieve this new conception of a self-regulating, self-governed universe requiring no supreme ruler or *ad hoc* causes and forces to keep it running.

Likewise we must remind ourselves that the nineteenth century conception of a purely mechanical universe of "atoms blindly running" is now obsolete, since there are many patterns, configurations and organizations in and through which the basic energy transformations appear and operate. There are, in other words, many persistent forms of order and organization and organism which have evolved in the billions of years of time, as we see in rocks or crystals and in living organisms. Thus while there are the disorderly molecules that give rise to statistical regularities as in gas laws, there are also these organized patterned processes and events, as exhibited by plant and animal organisms.

The great advances in our understanding of chemical processes come with the discovery that each compound or molecule is a spatial configuration wherein each atom has a specific location or position in the larger molecular configuration. Thus a compound of the same chemical composition might behave in totally different ways if the atoms shifted their position in the molecule, as in dextro- or levo-rotary compounds (which are mirror images of each other). Today stereochemistry is concerned not primarily with the older problem of how much, but with the question of where and how the atoms in the molecule are located, how they can be rearranged and recombined.

The electrons and the atoms have a capacity to act, react and interact in a number of different patterns or configurations of varying degrees of stability and permanence. These can combine into larger configurations which again act, react and interact to maintain further combinations within the range of their patterned activity.

What seems to be increasingly clear is that everywhere there is pattern, configuration or organization as the innumerable activities are constellated into the kind of structure and organizations we call crystals or colloids, and cells and organisms. A limited number of basic physical-chemical processes can be organized into an extraordinary range of different configurations, such as crystals, rocks and minerals, or gels and solutions, or cells and organs, within which different chemical compounds can be utilized for equivalent purposes.

Thus most animals use iron and plants use manganese for respiration. Most remarkable are the proteins, each of which has the same basic structural arrangement, as nearly as can be discovered, but by incorporating different chemical atoms at different locations within the protein molecule, many different proteins are produced, differing for each plant and animal, and, indeed, for each individual organism.

It is becoming clear that the same or equivalent pattern of configuration may be constituted with different materials, such as different chemical elements, or the same materials may be organized into different configurations. This is the key to the paradox, of relative simplicity but greatest diversity, arising from the operation of the basic processes within different spatial configurations and fields, utilizing different constituents to produce the amazing variety of different products, especially among organisms. It cannot be too strongly emphasized that the behavior of every single event, electron, atom, molecule, cell, organ or organism, is always patterned by the field in which it occurs. There are no isolated single events, since even a single quantum of energy cannot be released unless and until there is another configuration ready to receive it. There are no discrete, unrelated activities or self-acting agents or forces, because whatever exists and happens has an environment of other activities and events with which it is interrelated to form the configurations and patterns of existence.

The release of energy and its transformation can occur only within the configurations wherein two or more constituents interact. These configurations can become increasingly large by addition and repetition of the same patterns, as in a gas or a crystal or by new combination with other patterns as in aperiodic solids and organisms.

Nature is both stable and orderly but also plastic and flexible, capable of entering into new patterns and diversified combinations, as we see in the variety of structures and organisms of the geographical environment. But even these varied forms and products have not exhausted the possibilities and potentialities. Man today is synthesizing wholly new substances and forms, fabricating ever new tools and machines, creating new products and combinations that never before existed. This he can do by rearranging and recombining the physical, chemical and biological processes into new arrangements and new sequences. On each level of organization different possibilities appear as the constituent parts, by their interaction organize into new configurations in which those constituents behave differently as they participate in a different organization or field.

Furthermore, with increasing complexity, as in organisms, there is more and more possibility of selectivity that looks like choice or purposive activity, of weighing alternatives and making adjustments, of managing affairs with foresight and goal seeking.

Organization, as exhibited by the universe, or by an atom, by a simple cell or by a complex organism, appears as the way the several events, so-called parts or members, operate in such ways that they constitute the whole which in turn patterns their individual activities, through interrelated, synchronized and interconnected events.

Here we are beginning to recognize what is called a "field," which is hard to define because we have no language for such a situation or activity, no concepts yet formulated to indicate what a field means and does.

What seems to be clear is that activities, processes, events occur in configurations in which every constituent is actively engaged in the ceaseless transactions that make up and maintain that field. We cannot pick out any one constituent and endow it with special powers or treat it as the unique "cause," since what it is (its dimensions) and what it does are all to be viewed as products of the total field process which it, along with other constituents of the field, creates and maintains.

Here we find a statement by Einstein and Infeld very illuminating when they say: "It needed great scientific imagination to realize that it is not the charges nor the particles, but the *field in the space between* charges and the particles, which is essential for the description of physical events. . . . The theory of relativity arises from the field problem. . . . The contradictions and inconsistencies of the old theories force us to ascribe new properties to the time-space continuum, to the scene of all events in our physical world."

Every single electron, every single emission or radiation of energy, as well as every atom, molecule and larger configuration is, therefore, resonating in its field, actively participating in maintaining and operating a larger configuration and, thus, the universe.

The universe is now conceived, not as some tidy little restricted collection of planets and their sun, governed by arbitrary power or deterministic forces, but as a space-time manifold of almost unbelievable magnitude and a history going back towards, but never reaching, a beginning and a future of unlimited time, with a capacity for self-regulation and self-direction.

If once we can really grasp this conception, begin to realize the immense promise of this new cosmology, with its scarcely dreamed of potentialities, then we can begin to feel the great liberation and the inspiration it offers.

We can find in such a universe something so majestic and

awe-inspiring, that we can rightly feel in the presence of something bigger than ourselves, of something each of us as organisms shares in, has a part of, as through living we daily maintain our intimate interrelations with the geographical environment of nature. Thus we can begin to find the equivalents of what our older theological and cosmological beliefs provided, to make us feel secure and at home in an orderly world where there is purposive activity and where there can be goals and values.

We can find renewed courage and a new faith for living and for striving to realize the long-deferred goals of a democratic society, patterned according to the operations of a dynamic, ever-changing universe of which man himself is a part. In his endless search for the democratic way of life man can now find support from the universe, because the stars in their courses, the electrons and atoms proclaim that as the only way the universe continues to exist.

The geographical environment of nature, in which man exists as an organism, is one of the several environments in which man finds himself at once an active participant and also a spectator who by reflective thinking and by research is at long last beginning to feel at home.

III

The Internal Environment

WHEN WE SEE MAN AS *in* nature, not as a supernatural or un-natural being of our traditions, we will recognize that he is the most plastic and flexible, yet most stable and adaptable, expression of nature. We can then begin to understand him more clearly as an organism, as a product of that geographical environment.

The world in which man exists as an organism is, as described earlier, a dynamic, ever-changing complex, the active processes of which, while basically similar, have produced a great variety of products. As these processes have operated through millions of years, innumerable products have appeared.

While the basic geographical environment was arising, with the seas and land masses and the protecting atmosphere above, an extraordinary array of plant and animal organisms began to appear. What we call evolution is this continuous emergence of new forms or changing forms of existing organisms, each of which for a shorter or longer period of time has found in the geographical environment what it required for survival. We might say that the changing environment became constellated in a variety of organic configurations of greater or less stability and capacity for continued existence. Thus, the geographical environment of nature may be viewed as entering into these localized organic complexes, each of which has a capacity for selectively responding to and using that environment which it helps to maintain by its living processes.

It is indeed astonishing to review the great variety of such organisms that have appeared, some to play a relatively brief role in the drama of life and then become extinct; others to continue, more or less in their original form, or with minor modifications and adaptations which today are still existing unchanged after millions of years.

After innumerable other varieties of organisms had appeared, with structural and functional patterns, simple and complex, for living in various life zones and in different surroundings—water, earth and air—man appeared as another evolutionary product, but different from all other organisms.

To speak freely, it is as if, when evolutionary processes had reached a limit in the production of organisms of the existing patterns, man arose as a relatively new kind of organism. He derived from his mammalian ancestry the same basic biological functions and processes, but he was different from all preceding forms in having certain capacities: a flexibility and adaptability beyond others with few or no coercive instincts, but with a large brain capable of ideas, of imagination, of foresight, and of speech, with skillful hands for manipulating materials.

Man, therefore, appeared in the geographical environment, as the latest of organisms to evolve, equipped as no other
organism to try out a new pattern of existence and survival.

Every other species previous to man had met the problem
of survival by bodily differentiation and specialization of structures and functions and a highly selective process of utilizing
the environment. These adapations to the specific life zones or
medium in which the organism lived were often very effective.
The claws, the strong teeth, the horns and hoofs, the scales,
feathers or body armor, the streamlined structures, the fins and
wings, the capacity to live in water or to fly, to hibernate in
cold weather, all the various kinds of body protection and specialized parts for attack or fighting and the well developed capacities to find and use the specific foods offered by their life
zone—these were of great service in enabling an organism to
exist and to survive.

But these very specialized body forms and capacities
limited the organism to the more or less restricted life zone or
environment in which it could live with these specialized capacities and needs. Moreover, once differentiated and specialized, the different species could not change except in minor
adaptations of their fixed patterns as shown by the sea turtles.
Each species, as it were, reached the end of the evolutionary
road when it developed its peculiar body forms and specialized
parts. Many species, like the great reptiles, died out when, apparently, there was a large scale change in their environment
to which they could not adapt or from which they could not
escape to find what they required elsewhere. Others continued
to exist, each in its restricted life zone, relatively stable and unchanging over millions of years, as we see in the many forms of
organisms today which have almost the same structures and
functions as their remote ancestors ages ago, now preserved as
fossils.

Man came late into this already crowded earth where every

life zone was occupied by various species with specialized capacities for using the environment for survival. Man escaped the high price of specialization and, with his unique capacities for symbol creation and response, he kept open the road to continued development. Thus man did not adapt to nature, but rather he adapted nature to his own needs and purposes by creating a human way of life according to the meanings he himself imputed to nature and then learned to utilize for his own purposes. Thus he met the tasks of life, as we will see in the next chapter, by relying upon ideas, and tools and weapons, thereby keeping his organism plastic and flexible and capable of establishing his human way of living all over the earth, wherever he could find food and shelter and build a social order.

To understand how this was possible, we must try to understand what man derived from his mammalian ancestors, especially his amazing internal environment.

Here we must pause to realize what is rather difficult sometimes to grasp fully, namely, the conception of an organism which exists *in* an external environment, the geographical environment we have previously discussed, but who lives also *in* and *by* an internal environment. It is puzzling, at first, to think in these terms, to conceive of living processes as a sort of borderline of activities, between two environments, the internal and the external.

We have to stretch our minds to realize that all the complicated activities of living take place by a continual interrelation between the external and internal environment. Indeed, all living processes take place by a similar process of action, reaction and interaction, of transactions of selectively taking in and giving out, of transforming and converting the external into the internal and the internal into the external through various membranes, as we see in the cell's ceaseless activities. Indeed the interface or boundary has become the major focus of much research today as it is realized that all chemical processes and apparently all physical events take place in this in-between location, where the dynamic transactions of various energy configurations occur.

To understand man we must therefore recognize clearly how he exists as a process of continuous and fluctuating interchange between the geographical and the internal environment. The internalization of the environment gradually took place over millions and millions of years of slow evolutionary development. In the beginning of living organisms apparently the naked protoplasm was in direct, immediate contact with water and air, as we can see in very simple forms of slime molds. Only slowly did the early organisms develop an outer covering, a kind of envelope within which more and more of the external environment became incorporated. The early beginning of a stomach and intestines was a tube that began by a folding of the organism around a hollow space into which water carrying food particles flowed, as we still can see in many simple sea organisms such as the sponge, and also in embryological development where the process of evolution reappears to a large extent.

Apparently the blood began as a fluid, like early sea water, which was enclosed in this envelope and began to circulate around inside, where it still has the same balance of salts as the early seas.

While earlier and simpler organisms deposited their eggs in the water to be fertilized and allowed to develop at the mercy of the external environment, later organisms developed the capacity for fertilization inside the female, and later in the mammals, for the full development of the fertilized egg inside the female until the cub became capable of living in the external world. Yet in this process of gestation of the young, the fertilized egg and growing foetus still floats in a fluid, like his remote ancestors, as if the maternal uterus and the amniotic fluid were a protected little lake or sea, a duplication of the early external environment.

Thus every one of the many organ systems and processes, according to present knowledge of how evolutionary development took place, arose as a further development in the internal environment, a progressive incorporation of external processes and their elaboration into more and more specialized internal structures and interdependent functions which made possible functional transactions with that external environment.

It would take too long to rehearse the story of how each new species, building upon the achievements of its predecessors, then further elaborated or simplified the different functional activities, sometimes producing a more efficient, more economical organ or function by a dramatic variation from the previous pattern.

It seems clear from what is now known that the basic organic functions were variously attempted by different organisms as each developed its own internal environment of greater or less complexity, yet largely alike in their basic patterns because each was but a variation upon the general processes of organic functions.

Thus it is possible to trace back to ever more primitive forms most of the organ systems of mammals—the heart and circulation, the gastro-intestinal tract, the lungs, the kidneys, the liver, the reproductive organs (male and female and sometimes bisexual), the various glands of internal secretion, and the nervous system, including the brain (often only a small rudimentary collection of cells at the end of the nervous process).

What must be emphasized most strongly is that this internal environment arose by various evolutionary changes in which the internal environment maintained continuous but often indirect contacts with the external geographical environment, but in different patterns and combinations. Different organisms appeared and survived through this uninterrupted interaction of internal and external processes. It is obvious that they were dependent upon the external environment but equally they were dependent upon their internal environment, without which they could not utilize the resources outside for meeting their needs inside.

The more we reflect upon this process, the more it becomes necessary to think of an organism as an active field, with an outside and an inside—not two environments, but the same environment; what takes place outside and what takes place inside basically similar and reciprocal. Indeed, we can understand what takes place inside only by recognizing that it is the same natural environment, with the same basic physical, chemical and biological processes, only in each kind of organism they have been patterned and established in somewhat different structures and functional activities and interrelations.

It will help us to grasp this conception of an inner and an outer environment continually engaged in these circular processes if we will think of organism-environment as a "field" which is constituted by these circular processes called *transactions* by John Dewey and Arthur Bentley in *Knowing and the Known*.

These basic physical and chemical processes operate with altered dimensions when incorporated within organisms where their energy transformations are speeded up or slowed down, are interrelated and elaborated to meet the requirements and the possibilities of the cells in the internal environment. Thus we are beginning to recognize what is called bio-physics, organic chemistry and bio-chemistry as organic variations and elaborations of physical and chemical processes.

Now man's internal environment is probably the most highly elaborated and complicated and uniquely the most effective of all organisms. It derives from his mammalian ancestors, which had previously developed most of these functions to a high degree of efficiency. The special characteristics of the mammal for reproduction of the young inside the female and for feeding young by nursing had been evolved long ago. Likewise, almost all of the organ systems and functional processes of man—the wisdom of the body, as Walter B. Cannon called it—had been developed to a high degree of efficiency by earlier organisms.

Man, however, enjoys certain organic capacities which are superior to those of all other organisms. He has the most highly developed capacity for homeostasis—for maintaining his internal environment stable under varying external conditions, so that he can live in the extremes of cold or heat, at high altitudes or below sea level, thus having a greater range of life zones than any other species and a wider use of foods with a larger capacity for sustained activity even under adverse conditions. This superior ability to keep stable internally has enabled man to engage in a great variety of activities which other organisms can scarcely sustain. Moreover, it has given man a relatively greater freedom from the limitations of the external environment, since to a considerable extent, man can carry around his own stable internal climate aided by clothing and houses despite extremes of weather or climate. Also, man can regulate his organic functions for social living and can mobilize his reserves for prolonged or a single great effort apparently more effectively than other organisms.

In his capacity for maintaining a stable internal environment by a variety of processes and transactions with the external environment, man exhibits the dynamic self-equilibrating processes of the universe described earlier. He can not only exist as an organism but he can grow, develop, mature and age through these dynamic capacities of self-regulation and circular reciprocal transactions with the environment.

Man differs from other mammals also in his sexual activities; he is the only species whose sexual relations are independent of a seasonal period for mating or of a limited period of female heat. This means that human sexual activities are more or less continuous throughout the year, although there appears to be a diminishing fertility in the female during the hot summer months. One consequence of this is that babies are born throughout the year, and must be protected and cared for with shelter and stored food.

Another human characteristic is that the human has the longest period of helpless infancy, an infancy prolonged over years, as contrasted with the relatively quick maturation of other species. Likewise, the human has the longest period of adolescence.

But of major importance is man's large brain which has made it possible for him to develop language and symbols, to create ideas and tools and otherwise to live by intelligence as well as by organic memory. This large brain, however, has a profound influence upon his internal environment as well.

When we look more intently at man's internal environment, we find a number of organ systems, each performing its specialized functions in the internal environment which is highly organized and interrelated. This internal organization, like the organization we are discovering in the rest of nature, is not a relation of dominance and submission, of a governing or dictator organ exercising control over all others, as we have long been accustomed to think. The kind of organization we find is a patterned activity in which all the specialized organ systems and functional processes constitute the organization and maintain the organized whole by the way each articulates, synchronizes, compensates and otherwise operates in relation to all the others. The organization arises and is maintained, therefore, by the specialized constituent parts which thereby create the organized whole and this organized whole, in turn, reacts back upon the parts to keep them articulated and synchronized. This is the same kind of organization or field found in the atom, the molecule, the crystal and other orderly configurations and also in human society.

The various organ systems and functional processes in the body are like an orchestra of various instruments, each specialized in its form or structure and in its operation and what it produces and contributes to the whole. Thus each musical instrument is independent to the extent of being identifiable separately and specialized in its performance, but they are all interdependent in that they are played together and, by being played together and synchronized and adjusted to the kind and rate and quality of sound each produces in relation to all others, they become organized and give forth music. The sound each produces separately becomes blended, harmonized, contrasted and otherwise related, as in counterpoint, to the sound produced by the other instruments. It is worth noting that there is no tangible entity called organization in an orchestra—there are only the separate instruments and their players and the conductor who are brought into close spatial relations and play in an orderly, regulated way that we call organized. Moreover, no one single player or instrument or smaller group of similar instruments can produce the music which the whole orchestra can produce when playing together.

Another analogy may be used to illustrate this complex field we call organization, namely, a team of a number of players, as in baseball, football, etc. Each member of the team has been trained to perform certain kinds of patterned activities, always in relation to the activities of the other players. They come together, they disperse, they shift their formation, but always in ways that maintain the organized pattern of activities that distinguishes team playing from individual independent activity. Here again there is no specific, overall, tangible something that can be labelled as organization, which is to be viewed as a pattern of articulated, synchronized, activities in which specialized players perform their ever changing but specialized roles within the larger pattern. The team creates the organization by what each player does and this intangible organization in turn operates to guide, direct and largely control what each player does in relation to each other and to the team play as a whole.

This newer conception of organization recognizes this patterned circular way of operation in a field which is created by the participants and reciprocally governs their activities. This conception is essential to an understanding of how the internal environment is organized and maintained and how each separate organ system and functional process contributes to, derives from, and is responsive to, this organization of activities.

Within the internal environment there is a highly sensitive system of communication. There is the blood in its highly elaborated and progressively smaller channels through which it goes to and from every part of the body (except the outer cells of the skin and the eye and the outer parts of the hair and nails). The blood stream, continuously coursing out from the heart through the arteries and returning through the veins, carries to and takes away from every part of the body. In its course it receives at one location (lungs or intestines) what will be selectively filtered, taken out and absorbed or eliminated elsewhere, thereby maintaining a continuous channel of fluid communication throughout the internal environment. The blood, as one of the major processes of organization, is kept stable and uniform in composition within fairly narrow limits, except for certain rhythmic fluctuations and acute disturbances as in exercise, which reflect the total organic fluctuations around a stable level. This relative uniformity and stability of the blood is maintained by the activities of various organ systems which filter, refine, elaborate, detoxify, add, remove or otherwise regulate its composition. Thus the blood, as a system of communication, is dependent upon the lungs, kidneys and liver, for example, for much of its own regulation while serving to transport to those organs what they need for their functioning.

This reciprocal relationship of contributing to the maintenance of organs which in turn provide what the contributing organ or function needs, illustrates the basic character of biological organization where the parts maintain the whole which in turn pattern the activities of the parts, thereby giving rise to organization as a dynamic process.

The blood in itself is a highly complicated organization, with many different functions and capacities only partially understood. There are a number of different kinds of blood cells, red and white, and platelets, each of which plays a specialized role in the blood stream and in the internal environment. In general, the red cells, containing an iron compound called hemoglobin, carry oxygen, which they absorb in the lungs, to the cells and tissues of the body, thereby enabling these specialized parts to breathe, that is, to use oxygen in their functional processes. It is to be noted that the various cells which have become deeply incorporated within the organism, far from direct contact with the geographical environment, maintain communication with that external environment through the blood stream.

The white cells, in general, are the scavengers which police and maintain integrity of the blood stream and tissues when threatened by invading organisms or other dangers. Again, it will be noted that the various specialized cells of the body have lost some of their primitive capacity for self-defense and must rely upon the bloodstream for protection.

The more the blood cells are studied, the more their specialized functions and capacities are revealed in all their complexity and diversity, as each variety performs its specialized functions in the process of communication and protection.

Then there is, also, the blood plasma, with many different constituents and specialized functions, a continually changing reserve of what is needed by different organ systems and cells and other structures, and the carrier of various substances, which protect the organism from infections and the recurrence of a disease or provide needed chemicals, like hormones. Likewise, the plasma serves as one of the major agencies for keeping the internal environment stable and more or less uniform. This service it performs by a continuous process of balancing its own constituents, drawing upon the stored reserves of the organism or stimulating various organ systems to increased or decreased activity, to supply more or to eliminate any excess through the various channels of excretion, the urine, the faeces, the lungs and the skin.

There is a second channel of communication, the lymphatic system, in which fluids circulate among the different tissues and organ systems, acting as an auxiliary to the blood stream, supplying additional constituents, especially white cells, when acutely needed and otherwise keeping the different functions interrelated and coordinated. The lymphatic system has a series of small reservoirs, called lymph nodes, where invading organisms are filtered out and destroyed by the white cells, thereby providing a specialized protective service to cells and tissues. The lymphatic system may also distribute infections and malignant cells throughout the whole body.

The chief channel of communication for synchronizing and articulating the many ongoing processes internally and for enabling the organism to keep oriented and to react to and with the external environment, is the nervous system. Through highly specialized cells that have lost many of their primitive capacities, while developing an extraordinary sensitivity and a capacity, as a group of cells, to register previous experiences, the nervous system, with its nerve fibres, provides quick, flexible intercommunication throughout the whole organism. Here we see how man escaped organic specialization by developing the most highly specialized nervous system of all organisms.

The nervous system is specialized into many differentiated parts with local subsystems that directly coordinate different organ systems and functions and through various interconnections and relays pass on the resultants or summarized activity to the next group or on to the next larger segment. There are innumerable channels of communication among the different organ systems which are successively coordinated to function together and are either accelerated or retarded in their operation to synchronize with each other. There are other channels of communication which provide for the articulation and coordination of muscular movements. There are other channels of communication which enable the organism to maintain contact with the external environment by the operation of highly sensitized sense organs, such as the eye, the ear, the mouth, the nose and the skin; and then there is that unique collection of specialized cells in the brain through which these many activities, internal and external, are coordinated.

The nervous system and the brain are often compared to a telephone exchange, but even the most complicated automatic telephone system is crude and inefficient when contrasted with the amazing selectivity and functional capacities of the human nervous system, to be discussed later.

In this internal organization the glands of internal secretion are of major significance. Each of these glands produces a highly complex chemical substance or substances (called hormones) which is passed into the blood stream and carried through the organism. These substances are selectively absorbed by organ systems and cells in which they operate to stimulate or depress their functional processes. Each of these chemical messengers has a specialized potency to speed up or retard one or more processes, thereby bringing about an articulation and synchronization of functions for organic living. These glands operate as an interrelated dynamic system, balancing and compensating each other in the total organic functions of growth, development, maturing and reproduction, indeed all the processes of living.

Within each cell, there are one or more enzymes or catalysts which activate, regulate and synchronize the different processes that each kind of cell carries on, always interrelated to other cells and the whole body. Most of these living processes within cells and in body fluids operate by what is called an autocatalytic reaction, wherein a small quantity of catalyst, enzyme, or vitamin activates a process and is then released to repeat the process in a continuous cycle, thus carrying on a self-regulating activity in each of the several steps or stages in the sequence of functional processes. It is being shown that in living organisms the utilization of various nutrients takes place in a sequence of interrelated functional processes so that highly effective, economic utilization takes place at low temperatures and in a number of small intermediary stages. This slower and more complicated functioning is one of the characteristics of living processes in which, as pointed out earlier, the basic physical and chemical processes operate, but at different rates and at lower intensities, to produce what is required for organic functioning.

The living cells in the organism are surrounded by other cells, all in a fluid medium, of blood, serum and intercellular fluid.

Each cell is actively engaged in a continuous process of taking in and expelling, with a dynamic interchange of substances through the cell membrane. The cell, living within this permeable membrane in a fluid medium, is the prototype of the living organism which likewise exists by a similar interchange between the external and internal environments.

It is the operation of these channels of communication, the blood, the lymph and the nervous system, plus their various collaborators, like the hormones, which makes possible the high degree of organization of the many specialized organ systems, tissues and cells internally and the integration of organic activities toward the external environment. Thus each organ, each group of cells, each tissue and fluid can be reached by a message—a "to-whom-it-may-concern" message, as Norbert Weiner has aptly phrased it, which each selectively receives and interprets according to its functioning concerns and capacities.

Here it should be pointed out that specialization is possible only when there is organization, that is, some kind of interrelation, such as the simple one of a parasite and host or the ever more complicated interrelations of the mammalian organism, especially man. By organization, which means team play, or orchestration, the specialized parts or members lose or give up some of their generalized capacities, the ability to perform a variety of functions and actions, and rely or become dependent upon the specialized activities of others to provide for their needs and protection, thus making possible through group activity what no single cell, organ system, part or individual could achieve. It is as if when the different cells were enclosed within the organic envelope, they lost direct contact with the external environment and, therefore, had to depend upon other cells and tissues and fluids to bring to them what they needed from the external environment. Thus cells which are far from the surface are supplied with oxygen and with other nutrients by the blood stream, they are activated and kept oriented by the nervous impulses which come from other cells and from the external environment through the sense organs.

If the various cells are arranged in order of their increasing capacities, it will be found that they show increasing complexity of specialized structure and increasing dependency upon being served by others. Moreover, it will be found that while this specialization and complexity which makes for organization, enables the organism to perform an ever widening range of activities, it also makes the more complicated organism more vulnerable, more readily put out of action, because it is dependent upon the coordinated, synchronized activity of all its specialized parts for its total functioning. Thus every functional activity within the organism's internal environment, as well as every movement or reaction to the internal environment, are total organic processes in which, with varying degrees of involvement, all parts of the organism participate, either directly or indirectly. If any one part of the organism is removed or rendered inoperative or any function is impaired, there is a total organic readjustment to bring about a new pattern of articulation and synchronization. Fortunately, in man there is a large factor of safety which permits him to exist despite loss of some organs and functions and parts (eyes or arms).

To meet this ever present danger of being dis-organized, organisms have developed various ways of maintaining their functional integrity in the face of possible interference or deprivation or injury. In man there are many highly developed processes for maintaining the total organization intact and functioning. These are processes or functional activities involving storage of reserves to be utilized in time of need, also such reactions as the rise of body temperature, the increased production of white cells and certain hormones, and the innumerable alterations in the plasma and in the inter- and intra-cellular fluids in response to injuries, infections, intoxications, certain deprivations and other disturbances or interferences with the regularly orderly functioning of the organism.

It is becoming clear that an illness is the way the organism attempts to protect and maintain itself against invasion by other organisms (bacteria), foreign substances or other threats and dangers to its integrity. The disease process involves functional-structural alterations in certain cells, tissues, organs, fluids, bony structures, which at first may be slight and temporary.

If this first response is effective in protecting the organism and restoring equilibrium, perhaps on a different level or with an altered balance, these various organic alterations will be reversed and the organism will revert to more or less of its previous condition. It seems clear that every illness, however slight, leaves a more or less persistent residue or modification in the organism, including often a resistance to a recurrence of certain diseases.

If the organism is unable to meet the invasion or injury effectively, the alteration in certain cells, tissues or fluids, etc., may increase progressively to irreversible changes, as shown by pathological changes which sooner or later may be fatal to the organism. Here we see how the extreme reaction to a threat or danger on the part of one group of cells or a specific tissue or organ may be so great as to jeopardize and even destroy the whole organism. From this we may gain some understanding of the varied capacities of the living cells to defend and maintain themselves by various processes, including the production of embryonic types of cells which are more or less resistant or immune to the toxin or disease organism which has stimulated such changes.

As discussed later, the organism has what is called organic memory exhibited in various ways, as this capacity to resist disease and repair injuries, the capacity of the blood plasma to "remember" an earlier infection and thus to resist a second infection, or the capacity to remember an earlier disturbance and to react vigorously (sometimes overreact) to a recurrence, as in allergies or anaphalactic shock.

Research is increasingly revealing the complicated interplay of organic functions and discovering what extraordinary capacities the organism has for its own protection and repair if assisted or stimulated or otherwise enabled to mobilize these resources. Thus modern medicine is engaged in developing these specialized agencies which, like new drugs, serums, hormones, anti-toxins, anti-biotics, vitamin concentrates, etc., operate to stimulate or release organic functions for the protection of the organism or its recovery.

What should be emphasized is that modern medicine is concerned with understanding and beneficently interfering in the internal environment of the organism, relying upon the organism's varied functional processes and reserves, including surgical removal or alteration when necessary, to assist the organism in its attempt to ward off or recover from any disease or injury. In this, modern medicine is increasingly alert to the total organic reaction to the disease and to the remedies or treatment given to the patient. No one organ system or process can be treated as wholly apart from or independent of the others.

Every "part" of the whole organism is actively operating or functioning, each organ system and function collaborating with varying degrees of intensity to meet the needs of the total organism, as required. Thus to keep the internal environment stable within certain limits and to restore its equilibrium when disturbed, a series of compensatory processes operates which under increasing stress involves more and more of the total organic capacities. If there is a deficiency of oxygen in the tissues, for example, the breathing process will be accelerated with faster heart beats, increased circulation, release of reserves, and so on, with more and more processes being involved as the need for protection becomes more critical.

The internal environment is like the external environment —it is continually changing, maintaining a dynamic equilibrium by larger or smaller fluctuations and sometimes by violent alterations as it continues to oscillate between the limits of living existence. The internal environment of man has relatively small limits within which it can fluctuate, but the human organism has the most flexible and efficient processes for maintaining that internal equilibrium stable.

Thus man can live in a wider range of life zones than any other mammal. Man can endure high altitudes, wet or dry climates, exposure to rapid and sometimes wide ranges of weather, seasonal changes and the other events through which the earth maintains its dynamic stability.

These fundamental internal life processes and their coordination occur, as we say, automatically, that is, they take place by the interreaction among the different organ systems and through the several channels of communication which were evolved through millions of years of mammalian and pre-mammalian evolution.

All that living cells have learned, from the most primitive functions to the most recently developed capacities of the sensitive brain cells, has been incorporated into this most recently evolved organism, man.

Our human internal environment is, therefore, both primitive and highly developed, a truly amazing synthesis of all the experience of the most remote and more recent past, brought together in a functioning whole, capable of elemental processes such as eating, digestion and elimination and reproduction, and of such extraordinary activities as language, creating ideas and arts and making tools and machines, inventing techniques, as well as establishing orderly group living.

The major difference between machines and organisms is that an organism can repair and reproduce itself. Also a machine will operate only so long as its parts remain relatively unchanged—if a part, like a bearing, wears down, changes its original dimensions by bending or twisting, or breaks, the machine begins to falter and soon stops. By contrast, an organism exists and functions only by continual alteration, changing its parts (organs, tissues, cells and fluids) and by never-ceasing movements or deformations which change the dimensions of every part. The organism ceases to live when it no longer changes by making these continuous readjustments. Indeed, every functional process within the organism occurs by deformation and alteration of structure within the cell, among and between cells, in the shape and size of organs, in the ever-changing tonicity and shape of muscles, of tissues and of membranes. Everywhere in the internal environment there is ceaseless change as structures alter in functioning processes, transforming and expending energy, storing energy or converting and releasing it.

The whole organism is changing with varying degrees of rapidity and extent of replacement. All the different cells are being replaced at different rates except those cells of the central nervous system which apparently are not replaceable. The persistence of conscious memory may be due to these nonreplaced nervous cells. The blood cells wear out, are discarded and replaced by the million every day. The cells lining the gastro-intestinal tract, from the lips to the anus, are being constantly replaced, as are the cells of the skin. The cells in the kidney and the liver are likewise being replaced at different rates; indeed, all the different cells in the organism are being discarded and replaced by new cells, with more or less similar shape, size and capacities. After injury, the replacing cells may be more primitive and undifferentiated or more highly differentiated.

Perhaps the most amazing aspect of this cell replacement is shown by the repair of injuries or damage; after the impaired cells break down and are removed by the blood stream, new cells begin to appear, rebuilding the damaged tissue, often with little or no visible alteration, but sometimes with changes such as we see in scars or in callus formed around a broken bone. Sometimes the cells will congregate around a foreign body and build a protecting wall of cells or of some substance like calcium, which encloses the invaders and keeps them from interfering with the usual bodily processes. Sometimes the cells are unable to restore what has been damaged or has become atrophied and then the rest of the organism readjusts to that inactive part. Sometimes the cells cannot maintain an orderly arrangement and become wild and anarchistic, as in cancer cells.

Tissues, like muscle fibres, also are being continually altered, growing larger and stronger, or smaller and weaker in response to use and nutrition. Indeed, there is in most organ systems and tissues and even bony structures to some extent, a reserve capacity, enabling the organ or tissue to enlarge when needed to meet demands, and also a capacity to shrink when not in use.

These continual replacements of cells and tissues are remarkable, but they are only the gross expression of what is taking place on a finer scale in the replacement of the chemical constituents of the whole organism. As pointed out earlier, chemical composition of the organism is being reconstituted day after day. This means that every atom in the organism, in the cells, in the tissues, in the fluids, with greater or less rapidity, is being replaced, the old atom being discarded and eliminated and its place being taken by a new atom of similar chemical element or sometimes a different element. Sometimes the cells and tissues in an organism, as in aging, cannot select and retain what they need or cannot release and eliminate what they should replace. Sometimes they retain too much or release too much, and again they may also lose the capacity to restore what they need. Aging, therefore, may be viewed as the cumulative change in an organism whose basic capacities of self-maintenance have been altered or lost.

The organism, therefore, is engaged in this endless process of taking in, selectively absorbing, utilizing and rejecting the various chemical substances that constitute its different parts and fluids; meanwhile it is maintaining its specialized structure and functions. Thus, we have the seemingly stable, enduring organism, which from day to day looks as if it were unchanged, but which is undergoing these continuous alterations in its basic composition. The amazing aspect of this process is that not only every replacing cell but every new, replacing atom fits into the appropriate place and activity and so plays its specialized part in the organism, carrying on the functional processes necessary for the existence of the organism and maintaining the relatively unchanged external appearance.

Here again we see how the internal environment, like the geographical environment of which it is a part, exists and operates by a dynamic, ever-changing equilibrium, as shown by the ceaseless activity within each molecule and atom. It is as if the geographical environment were ebbing and flowing through the organism, as these chemical atoms enter into and later are released from the living organism. This becomes more easily understood when we realize that the living process is just this ceaseless activity, that cannot stop without terminating the life of the organism. Indeed, death is the cessation of living processes which may take place in one or more organ systems or parts of the organism and sooner or later involve the rest.

From recent studies it appears that there is an orderly, regular process of growth, development, maturation and aging, a sequence of changes beginning at conception through which every organism must pass. It is as if each individual must travel along the same broad highway.

But it is also clear that each individual human organism, with its specific heredity and its individual nurture and care will pass through those sequential changes, will travel along that highway, at his or her own rate of progress. Each will attain the size, shape, weight, functional capacities, will grow and mature rapidly or slowly, will begin to age, according to his or her idiomatic pattern.

There are orderliness and recurrent regularities in human organisms but there are also wide differences and highly individualized expressions of those basic processes.

It is evident that what we call development and growth and aging are possible because of this organic capacity to change, to modify itself, even to produce different cells and organ systems, as we see in the development before birth of the infant, starting as a single cell egg which, when fertilized, begins to multiply and divide and then to differentiate into different kinds of cells, arranged in various patterns that form the organ systems and so make possible the total organism with its diverse functions.

For such development and for the growth in size and shape, the organism must be capable of absorbing and retaining what is necessary to permit multiplication of cells, differentiation of cells, accumulation of reserves over and above what it must utilize for current living.

The most remarkable of all these living processes is this capacity of cells to reproduce their own kind, including the ability to reproduce much the same kind of organism. The way in which organic memory that we call heredity operates is not yet understood, although it has been shown that in the original egg cell and sperm are the chromosomes or carriers of the genes in which this memory is believed to be located as the capacity to keep cells and organisms true to their type. This capacity is difficult to understand because it operates to maintain the specialized form and function in every cell of the organism, although in the course of that organism's life there may be untold generations of such cells, as one generation of cells is replaced by the next. Moreover, it operates while the individual organism is developing before birth and continues throughout the life span, controlling the growth and maturation, the repair and replacements, the aging of the organism over a period of years. In old age the genes sometimes appear to get "tired" and lose their control, as shown by curious growths, especially in the skin.

This capacity is exhibited by the germ cells, coming from the ovary in the female and the testes in the male, where it operates to produce the eggs and the sperms with their fixed quota of chromosomes, with genes, which are variously assorted and combined when the sperm and egg meet in fertilization and in cell division. Thus the heredity process provides for a high degree of regularity and uniformity from generation to generation and within the life of a single living organism. But it also permits variations and deviations since each egg and sperm will have a somewhat varying assortment of genes derived from the ancestral store and they will combine in different ways, depending apparently upon their location in the chromosomes.

Thus, through this process we shall call heredity, the organism can grow, develop and mature, undergoing the continuous alterations and replacements in cells and in chemical constituents, yet continue to exist as apparently the same identifiable organism and produce descendants which will resemble their parents.

Since man has few or no instincts, as contrasted with other organisms, he is less subject to the coercive control of inherited reflexes and patterns, and thereby is free to create and change his activities. This plasticity and flexibility, especially in infancy and childhood, are of immense significance because they permit man to learn and to be culturized and socialized, as will be discussed in later chapters.

What is inherited may be conceived as the pattern or configuration within which growth, development, maturation and aging, also procreation, will take place. Thus we may think of inheritance as a process taking place in a "field" or perhaps as the field itself which governs the life career of the organism, maintaining the pattern of organization, the selective utilization of the environment and the role which the organism will play in its life zone.

But the organism is also guided and controlled in its functional activities by organic memory, by the way the cells and tissues and organ systems learned to cooperate within the total organism. These lessons were learned by our mammalian ancestors and before them by the other organisms which developed the first of these physiological functions and then elaborated and refined them and organized them into a functioning whole that is reproduced in every new generation.

We are the inheritors of all this learning which our genes and our organ systems "remember" from the dim past. It is startling to stop and think of where we derived each of our different organ systems and functioning processes—what organism "invented," so to speak, each of our organ systems and functions as a way of carrying on the life process. We are born with this wisdom of the body, as the late Dr. Walter Cannon called it, because throughout the long period of organic evolution, this ability to function in each of these specialized ways and to coordinate with other functions was developed by specialized cells and organs, tissues and fluids, and became established as organic memory, or heredity.

The various cells and organ systems of the human body remember not only the patterns of activity learned long ago by our prehuman ancestors but they also remember much of what they have experienced during the lifetime of the individual organism. Thus we carry around within us a continuous, unbroken memory of everything we have experienced, but only a small fraction of those memories is accessible to us, can be recalled, as we say. But the various cells and organ systems remember and continue to react as their memories largely dictate, and we as organisms benefit from these organic memories and the wisdom they have fostered.

Also, from our organic memory we derive the capacity to mobilize our reserves for emergencies. Thus if we are invaded by disease-producing organisms, we can call upon a variety of processes to protect us from the invaders, and these operate efficiently according to the patterns learned long ago. Moreover, once we have had a disease and have overcome it, our blood stream remembers. If we had whooping cough, for example, as an infant or young child, all the rest of our lives the blood serum will remember and will continue to keep us immune or resistant to that disease. Indeed, the blood remembers more faithfully than we do what we have experienced, although it is probable that all the original constituents of the blood have been replaced many times. It reacts, often vigorously, to some long past irritation or damage, as we see in allergies which are learned patterns of reacting to foreign substances.

Another valuable lesson the organism learned long, long ago which the body remembers is the capacity to mobilize against danger, threats or pain. This total organic reaction which we call emotional response is a beautiful expression of the organization of the body, wherein every function is co-ordinated and synchronized to provide the maximum capacity to fight or flee from attack, or to escape by other means.

Since emotions play such a large part in human living and are such a dramatic disturbance in the internal environment, their mode of operation should be examined in detail.

Every response of the organism involves some alteration of its physiological state and the magnitude of its various functional processes. When these disturbances direct his conduct or became intense, we call them emotions.

When the infant is born, he has, if normal, a fully developed capacity for emotional reaction. If provoked, he gets angry and begins to rage—his heart beat accelerates, his blood pressure goes up, his breathing is faster, the blood is withdrawn from the interior to the muscles and surface of the body, the liver releases glycogen (for blood sugar), and adrenalin and other chemicals are passed into the blood. Every organ system, every functional process and all bodily reserves are progressively called upon to enable the organism to meet the emergency. This has been called the alarm reaction or a state of vigilance.

When in that condition, the organism becomes a primitive mammal, fully aroused and prepared for violent activity of gross movements but unable to exercise what we call judgment, discrimination or fine adjustment. That is why we call such a state a "blind rage" and refer to overmastering anger, or paralyzing fear.

We are indeed carried away by strong emotions which in the past often saved us from disaster. But when strongly emotionally aroused, we are in a state of panic when these organic reactions take over control of our actions without thinking or reasoning.

Emotional reactions are indeed primitive. They are basic organic functions, part of our mammalian inheritance, like hunger and eating, or sexual impulses. Like these other functions, the emotions are subject to various kinds of alterations and modifications, as we will discuss later when discussing the cultural and social environments.

There are several modifications of emotional reactions which should be recognized here because they have such far-reaching significance for the internal environment.

When an individual has been subjected to an emotional provocation, that experience may render the individual more sensitive to a repetition of such a provocation, so much so that he may become continually alert, prepared to react to a possible recurrence. Thus if a child has been frightened by a barking dog, a return to the place where that occurred or the sight of the dog at a distance may touch off a panic in the child. Sometimes merely going near the place where the original fright was experienced, with no dog in sight or within hearing, will arouse fear in the child. Apparently when emotionally disturbed, the individual becomes sensitized to any part of the original experience and can be again disturbed by the reappearance of such a part or of the location, even if there is nothing threatening. It is as if the organism having once been endangered remembers to be on guard, and thereafter acts by anticipation of what it has learned to expect, as the blood stream will mobilize its resistance when again exposed to infection.

This capacity for remembering and for reacting *as if threatened* probably served to protect individuals from potential danger or at least to make them alert and wary, just as a horse who has been frightened at a particular place on the road will tend to "shy" every time he passes the spot. An individual may, after one or more disturbing experiences, become continually watchful, as Howard Liddell has suggested, always on guard against a possible recurrence of that threat.

But this sensitivity may also handicap the individual who may be unnecessarily cautious or fearful, even to the extent of being unable to perform simple acts or go to familiar places because of some accidental event which has sensitized him. Moreover, an individual may become more or less permanently antagonistic toward someone who has accidentally been involved in the individual's being angry; thereafter he will react to that person's presence as to an enemy to be resisted or attacked.

Another modification of emotional reactions is of major importance in the internal environment, although it is difficult to explain how this takes place. When a person is faced with an ongoing emotion-producing situation, continually being threatened or hurt or frightened, but unable to escape or to defend himself, like a child with a severe or cruel parent, or living in a situation of repeated threats or attacks, he cannot go on "emoting" all the time. Emotional reactions use up the organism's energy and after a prolonged reaction of anger or rage or fear, the organism becomes exhausted. Moreover, to live, the individual thus exposed must eat, eliminate, sleep and engage in various activities from time to time, while maintaining a state of watchfulness.

Under such circumstances what apparently happens is that the acute emotional reaction, the more or less violent, all-over response, becomes a chronic state of emotional tension, a sort of milder but prolonged reaction of lesser intensity, an active but diminished vigilance.

Anger becomes resentment or hostility toward the world, often expressed in disguised or indirect activities or disturbed functions.

Fear becomes anxiety or guilt, as we call those continuing bodily states of expectation of danger which we can carry around inside our organism. Thus we can feel resentment against others which we do not openly show or we can feel anxious about possible danger or guilty about what we have done or expect will happen to us, but go on with our usual activities. Outwardly the individual may be polite and suave, show no signs of being disturbed, yet feel resentful and hostile; or he may be very anxious while appearing poised and brave to others.

It is as if the readiness to act, the watchful expectation and chronic emotion, instead of being expended in outward reactions against the world, were localized internally and focused into some muscular set or narrow channel of expression that may be a complete disguise or substitute for release.

Sometimes this chronic resentment or anxiety or guilt which cannot come out into action or speech, becomes "localized" or focused in an organ system or functional process, such as the gastro-intestinal tract, or heart and circulation, or lungs, or other organs, like the sexual organs. There the localized reaction or condition appears as a dysfunction or disease such as a stomach upset or gastric ulcer, high blood pressure, too rapid and unsteady heartbeats, asthma, skin disorders, headache, even colds, all being expressions of these chronic or repressed emotions that cannot be released and so operate to disturb bodily functioning.

Experiments on various animals—dogs, cats, pigs and sheep —have shown how these dysfunctions, these disturbed organ systems, or illnesses, can be established by giving the organism a shock, or by provoking emotional reactions in the organism but not allowing it to express or release the emotion, or by presenting the organism with a problem it cannot solve or building up a watchful state of expectation of pain. Thus in the laboratory it is possible to duplicate much the same conditions and disturbances which the physician finds in individual human patients, as persistent modification of the internal environment.

But, as pointed out earlier, man is unique in being flexible, plastic, unspecialized except in his nervous system, especially his brain, with skillful hands and a capacity for speech, ideas and imagination. Man is highly specialized in the sensitive cells, which, like the bark on a tree, cover the upper surface of the human forebrain and can function in a unique way to make possible a great variety of activities of which no other organism is capable. Here we have a development of cells which exhibit the greatest complexity of functions except perhaps those found in the germ cells. These brain or cortical cells operate much like the germ cells in that they serve to regulate, to guide and to integrate the total organic activities, mediating between, within and without.

The earlier picture of the brain as a sort of dictator which bossed the organism, like a ruler issuing orders to his subjects, is being replaced by a conception of the brain as the focal center for articulating, coordinating, synchronizing, regulating and otherwise balancing the various specialized parts and functions for working in harmony and unison, by providing rapid intercommunication among all these functioning parts, reconciling and resolving possible conflicts or interferences, speeding up or slowing down and otherwise maintaining an ever-changing, dynamic equilibrium within the internal environment and adjusting overtly or by ideas and feelings to the external environment. These cells have a unique capacity for memory of what has been experienced by the human organism, so that the individual can utilize some of his past experience in the present and can by anticipation prepare for the future. Much of what is registered in the brain cells as memory is not accessible to the individual, although experimental study has shown that what has been "forgotten" can sometimes be recalled when the individual has been hypnotized and "put back" to an earlier period in his life career.

These brain cells have made possible the development of language, the use of subtle symbols and the creation of ideas which are expressed in words that operate to guide and direct the individual's conduct and feelings. Indeed, as will be pointed out later, man lives primarily by ideas, these imaginative pictures of the world and of himself by which his activities are oriented, often in conflict with the actual world of events.

But with this capacity to form ideas and create tools and techniques, man has kept himself more or less flexible and plastic, as a species capable of modifying his ways of life but always within this human pattern. But this very flexibility and capacity for living by ideas which he imposes upon the actual world of the geographical environment and upon his own functions and actions, may also lead to disaster.

The same capacity for creating ideas, for inventing new forms and patterns, for anticipating what is to come and for remembering what has been experienced, may lead the individual into difficulties when the ideas and beliefs he relies upon for comfort or escape or self-justification become obsessions or compulsions or when his imaginative creations become too disordered or in conflict with the prevailing ideas and conduct of his group. Thus he may destroy himself by the very capacity that has made human living possible.

This is the paradox of human life: the same capacities and functions may serve to protect and guard man, provide him with safety, comfort, with fulfillment of his needs and desires; or they may lead to self-defeat through disease, individual distortion, or to social disorder and destruction. Likewise in the geographical environment the same processes and events may operate to produce beneficent or destructive results.

IV

The Cultural Environment

THUS FAR WE HAVE BEEN LOOK-
ing at the geographical environment and the internal environment in and through which the living processes occur. But while
man, as a mammalian organism, exists within the geographical
environment and maintains his internal environment by continual transactions with the external, he lives in a human world
of his own creation. This human world we may call the cultural environment, not separate and distinct from the internal
and external, already discussed, but rather as another dimension of the environmental field.

In order to grasp this cultural environment, without being
confused by our customary ideas, we need a wider and deeper
perspective to give us a new approach to the overly familiar

scene. This we may find by looking at the world and man in the following terms.

All over the earth, as we have seen, the same fundamental processes, physical, chemical and biological, are operating. What we call nature, the geographical environment earlier discussed, is highly regular and almost uniform, despite the local differences in landscape, of mountains or plains, or desert or jungle, of climate and weather, of arctic cold and tropic heat, and the local variations in plants and animals. Beneath these differences the same physical processes are operating: gravitation, magnetism, electricity, heat, radiations, etc.; likewise the chemical reactions are basically similar. And different plants and animals live by the same biological processes all over the earth. Nature everywhere is fundamentally alike.

All over the earth human beings are essentially alike. Despite differences in color, size, shape and some variations in physiological capacities and functions, all mankind belongs to the same "human race," derives from the same mammalian ancestry, and has the wisdom of the body with the same basic functions of nutrition, elimination, gestation, etc., and so has much the same or equivalent organic needs. Everywhere human nature is essentially similar.

Yet, despite this regularity of nature everywhere and this essential similarity of human nature in all mankind, we find different groups of people living in different cultural worlds, which they have created and imposed upon nature and themselves. Each group of peoples has transformed its local geographical environment into the kind of world it cherishes according to its ideas and assumptions. Each group has also transformed its own members into the kind of persons we call Hindu, Chinese, Japanese, Russians, French, Italians, Spanish, Germans, Swedes, Finns and Norwegians, English, Irish, Scotch, Arabs and so on, in each of the larger historic cultures, not forgetting the innumerable smaller groups of so-called primitive peoples.

How does this happen? How can we understand the amazing diversity of ways of life, these different designs for living which have been developed by different groups of people with the same human nature in the same natural environment?

As we have previously pointed out, man, as an organism, exists in the geographical environment we call nature; his internal environment must maintain contact with that external environment in and through continuous transactions for living and for survival.

From his earliest days as man, he has faced various life tasks, persistent problems which he must continue to meet so long as he exists as man.

1. In order to live and to survive, he must come to terms with the geographical environment, to get food, to find shelter, to meet danger and enemies and otherwise to guard himself and his young from the hazards of life.

2. To live more or less peacefully with others and to permit the division of labor made desirable, if not necessary, by his tools and techniques and also by the birth of young throughout the year (instead of a single period for births), he had to develop and maintain some kind of patterned group living or social order.

3. For such group living he must regulate his functional processes and curb his impulsive behavior and emotions, by transforming his organic needs and his naive behavior into orderly, patterned, purposeful conduct.

As pointed out before, man is unique in that he did not follow other organisms and develop a specialized body for meeting the requirements of existence. Instead of adapting to the environment by differentiation and specialization of his organism for a restricted life zone like other organisms, man kept himself relatively plastic and flexible. He specialized in his nervous system and relied upon ideas and tools and weapons to meet these persistent tasks of life. He approached nature and human nature not as fixed and unchangeable factors to which he must adapt, but as capable of being selectively used and manipulated for a human way of life. Thus, he began to create his human cultural worlds according to his beliefs and assumptions about the universe and man, and to fit them into those beliefs.

It is important to understand as clearly as possible what this involves. Man with his capacity for thinking, for speaking, for imaginative ideas, unlike other organisms, did not adjust to nature, but rather he selectively utilized nature for meeting his life tasks as he conceived nature. This he did by viewing the world according to the meaning he himself perceived therein and then guiding all his activities by those meanings. He organized his experience by his ideas and beliefs and began to manipulate events and direct his own conduct according to what he assumed and expected.

Only a dynamic world of basic processes which can and do produce a variety of diverse products, only a world of many possibilities would allow man to develop so many different cultural worlds as we find all over the earth. In a very meaningful sense, we can say that nature has been very patient of man, allowing him to impose his many different ideas and assumptions upon the geographical environment and upon his internal environment, to produce these different cultural worlds.

Only an organism like man, with an internal environment derived from his mammalian ancestry, stable but flexible, largely self-regulatory but capable of being adapted to a variety of ways of living, only an organism with a large brain capable of developing ideas, language, and tools, of imagination and daring, with skillful hands to make tools and weapons, could create such cultural worlds and accommodate himself to these self-imposed requirements and limitations, finding in its permitted activities and its goals the fulfillments of his organic needs which he himself has shaped into his desires and aspirations.

Each cultural world is a selection from the many possibilities offered by nature and a selection among the many potentialities of man. Each cultural world recognizes and utilizes only some aspects of the geographical environment and ignores all others, just as it cultivates and elaborates some of man's capacities and functions and ignores or represses others. As might be expected, each group utilizes the geographical world with its immediate specific landscape and climate and its local plants and animals in its cultural formulations and mode of living, but different groups may treat the same plants and animals in different ways, as shown by the different treatment of cows by the English and by the Hindus.

Man's cultural worlds arise from his patterned, selective transactions with the environment. Thus the same process is at work as exhibited by different organisms living in the same life zone but selectively responding to and utilizing what that life zone offers for their specific needs and capacities. It is the same environment, yet each organism finds in it what it has learned in its evolutionary development to see, to hear, to use and to reject. Man approaches that natural environment also in his selective way and transforms it into a cultural world by the meanings he imposes upon it.

How did these cultural worlds arise and flourish? How did they get started? No one knows and probably we can never find out, because the first early steps were taken long, long ago before man made any records or developed any oral traditions. We can, therefore, only infer, surmise, try to picture imaginatively from what little is known from archeological findings, how the process began.

If man were to develop a human environment and live in a world of his own creation, not merely exist as an organism on the level of physiological functions and organic impulses like other organisms, he had to make certain assumptions, create certain conceptions, about the world and man to guide him toward purposeful activity for such a human world. He had to treat the world and direct himself, to act, to think, to believe, to feel on an *as if basis*—as if the world and man were what he assumed them to be, what he hoped, feared and wanted them to be and to do, in order to achieve his purposes.

Thus, it seems probable that he gradually developed a body of conceptions of the world and of man which we can describe and categorize as follows, remembering that these are an intellectualized statement of what began as exploratory action and only slowly became patterned and formalized.

1. The Nature of the Universe—how it was created and how it is operated, by what power, authority or control; what makes things happen, for his good or his ill; and how can he come to terms with the power or controlling force for his own needs. Upon this assumption he could develop his relation with the geographical environment for getting food, shelter and safety in a world often precarious and threatening, both generous and reluctant to yield what he sought.

2. The Place of Man in That Universe—his origin and his destiny; his place in, or outside of, nature; his relation to the power or authority which rules the world.

3. The Place of the Individual within the Group—his relations to the group and to other individuals; "his rights, titles, obligations and interests" and his status; "who shall be sacrificed for whom."

4. Human Nature and Conduct—man's image of himself as good or evil, or as capable of both, and his beliefs about what he should and should not do, especially in human relations.

These four basic conceptions are ways of ordering and interpreting man's experiences. They provide the assumptions upon which different groups of men could undertake to meet their persistent life tasks, approaching nature and human nature *as if* they were what they believed. In terms of these conceptions each group could develop a human way of life, learning purposeful conduct addressed to the meanings and purposes, the values and aspirations which these assumptions made desirable or necessary aspects of nature and of man.

Moreover, these assumptions guided man into inventing and applying his weapons, tools and techniques for fighting, hunting, fishing, finding and growing food, developing agriculture and animal husbandry, building shelters, and other practices for manipulating the environing world and the various materials, plants and animals it offered.

Purposeful conduct, the pursuit of values, the utilization of tools and techniques all necessitate concern for the consequences of what one does and says. Thus in human development we see the growing awareness of the consequences of all activities, with increasing efforts to focus and refine action toward the consequences desired and to avoid what is not desired or must be prevented.

This development of tools, techniques and weapons along with the ideas and assumptions of his culture directed man's efforts to establish and maintain orderly group living and to rear and educate his young to exhibit the kind of conduct required for maintaining that kind of group life. Since of all organisms the human has the longest infancy, the child remains relatively plastic and capable of learning for several years, thereby making it possible for the parents to indoctrinate their children in the patterns of their group. Thus traditions are perpetuated from generation to generation and the young learn to live in the world as defined by their elders.

Each group later formulated and expressed these four basic conceptions in what we call religion, philosophy, law and custom, including myths and folklore with its ways of thinking about events and also the arts. Each group has elaborated its formulations, with different emphasis upon one or more of these four conceptions. Thus, each group differs in its expression of the several assumptions about the universe, its creation and way of being operated, as we may see in the various theologies all over the world, some with their beliefs about supernatural powers and deities and others non-theistic.

But in each group all four conceptions are interrelated and interdependent, each reinforcing and deriving sanction from the others, so that there is a more or less coherent, integrated body and system of ideas and thinking which are cherished as the fundamental truths or final answers to these basic questions, which all must accept as such.

Upon these interrelated beliefs each of the larger groups has established its society or social order, with some kind of government or authority-wielding body or person, which dictates the rules and enforces them, settles disputes and otherwise directs the group life, always guided by these traditional beliefs. Likewise, each group has developed the symbols and rituals for the prescribed activities in different circumstances and for different occasions and events, including the prescribed practices for all interpersonal relations upon which the social environment and kinship are built.

In brief, acting upon these basic assumptions and guided by these beliefs, man has created his symbolic, cultural worlds of meanings and values which, like a screen or pattern, he has interposed between, or imposed upon nature and himself so that he sees everything, thinks about everything, acts toward everything and every person, including himself, largely in terms of these self-created and self-imposed meanings and purposes.

Thus, man's cultural world is a man-made creation, another dimension of the environment, selectively established and interpreted from among the many possibilities and perpetuated by man himself. It is part of nature because it was created by man and does not exist as anything superhuman or supernatural. But it is different from the rest of nature, just as a machine is different: a machine never existed until man invented it, but it is natural in the sense that the machine is a new, selected arrangement, combination and sequence of processes that never before were brought together and operated for that purpose. Every new tool or machine and new product indicates the amazing plasticity of nature, the seemingly unlimited number of different ways in which the basic physical, chemical and biological processes can be organized, focused and directed to produce different products.

In the same way the cultural environment may be distinguished from the geographical environment; it never existed until man created it, but it is natural, being a selected version of the ongoing geographical environment, a more or less unique patterning of events never before brought into such a complex or operated and used for such purposes.

Here we are liable to go astray because we have certain traditional beliefs about these cultural worlds derived from early assumptions which until recently made us think of culture, with these patterns and these assumptions, in terms almost impossible to understand, except as mysterious or magical, as supernatural in origin or un-natural and superhuman, or what we call subjective.

Thus for centuries we have interpreted human thinking, knowing, speaking as some kind of subjective, psychic, un-natural activities, and assumed that knowledge of the world involved something with a unique status or special kind of existence—a sort of third order of events between man and nature. Accordingly all of man's ideas and beliefs, his knowledge, and his cultural traditions have been treated as mysterious superhuman or extra-human entities. This has given rise to the varied problems of philosophy, like epistemology, etc., and of psychology, like cognition, mental activities, many of which problems are now being reformulated or dismissed as no longer valid problems in the light of our growing understanding of how man and nature are interrelated, through such transactions as human knowing and human acting and feeling. By this radical revision of our ideas, we can, as Dewey and Bentley have shown, in *Knowing and the Known*, clarify many of our persistent perplexities and avoid the long continued confusions of our intellectualistic traditions.

We must try to think about culture as one of the dimensions of man's environment which he has himself created, organized and established, just as he has invented language, with names for objects and events and relationships. When we give a name to something, the name does not become an independent entity and it does not change the object to which it is applied, although many have so believed. The name and the definition it carries operate to modify man's behavior—he acts toward the object so named according to the meaning conveyed by that name as he has learned to use and understand it. The word, the name, is a symbol, a signal to act in a certain way, a sign of what to expect from or to believe about the thing or person so named.

Likewise, when we make sentences about objects or events, we do not change the object or event—we communicate to others, or to ourselves, what we believe is the meaning of the situation, the relation of one thing or person to another, its characteristics, and so on. The sentence operates to modify human behavior, the way we or others will think, or act, or feel toward the objects or situation, which is not itself affected by these words (but may be altered by the activities stimulated by these words).

The culture world is, therefore, a highly complicated and elaborated set of patterns and symbols which guide, direct, control and enrich human behavior according to the basic assumptions and beliefs of each group. It affects the environment and man only in so far as it patterns human activities toward the environment, as in tools and techniques and toward other men and the individual himself.

What is of great significance is that man's cultural worlds gave nature and man himself, especially his various functions and activities, pattern and form, intensity and values which have enriched and embellished living. Because he has a large brain, capable of ideas and imagination, man with his relatively long life quickly wearies and becomes bored with his own organic necessities—eating, sleeping, eliminating and repeated sexual intercourse. When they become patterned and elaborated into rituals and ceremonies and made less accessible or even prohibited except on special occasions, they become invested with value and meaning, create tension and expectancy and often yield greater consummations when attained.

Thus, each culture has used some of man's functional needs and processes, his various capacities and potentialities, to maintain its cherished way of life; each culture has transformed the various organic needs for food, drink, elimination, sleep, sex functioning, into patterned, purposive conduct which may lead to fulfillment of that organic need, but only after various preparatory acts and embellishments that have often become goals or purposes in themselves.

Moreover, each culture provides a variety of interests, enjoyments, heightened pleasure by various devices: setting up barriers or obstacles to immediate approach or use or enjoyment and providing after each deferment an elaborated ritual or practice, such as fasting and feasting to make eating more enjoyable, sex taboos and deferred sex relations to heighten desire and limit intercourse to prescribed periods and ceremonies, and an extraordinary variety of sex play, coquetry, and erotic embellishments to enrich the bare act of coition.

The human body has been subjected to almost incredible manipulation and deformation, to distortions and mutilations of various parts and ornamentation by every possible means of decorating the skin, nose, ears, genitals and hair and nails, plus clothing and adornments of metal and animal parts, like skin and furs and teeth and feathers.

Eating and sex relations have been the chief foci of man's inventive mind. Next to weapons and fighting, he has lavished his artistic abilities upon food and drink and intercourse, creating all manner of imagination-stirring ideas and fantasies to increase, by anticipation, the range of such fulfillments from his organic functions, and to defer his consummations. In some cultures defecation has been made the occasion for elaborate rituals. Likewise, sleep has been patterned and elaborated in various ways to give this daily function a special setting. In some cultures man has developed a variety of patterns for breathing, relaxing, controlling heartbeats, and so forth.

Since this process of transforming organic needs and physiological functions is the unique achievement of man, the specific operations involved should be clearly recognized if its full significance is to be grasped.

Thus the newborn infant must begin to breathe, taking in air and expelling air in order to provide needed oxygen and to eliminate carbon dioxide. This respiratory process must continue without stopping so long as the organism lives. But as the baby grows he increasingly utilizes breathing for crying and sobbing, then for talking, singing, for communication and all the verbal approaches and preliminaries for social life, including smiling and laughing.

The primitive tactual sensitivity and need of the mammalian infant to be cuddled and mothered (licked and nuzzled among infra-humans) may be transformed into a variety of more or less highly individualized requirements for specific kinds of tactual stimulation and soothing, such as masturbation, stroking blanket, rubbing ears, etc. Much of infantile sexuality seems to be an expression of this tactual need and response to tactual contacts that becomes more or less dormant in childhood, to be revived in adolescence and become one of the major forms of expression and fulfillment in adult sexual relations.

Eating is an essential process to provide needed food for nutrition of the organism. But eating becomes patterned, regulated and transformed into a great variety of activities—feasting, fasting, rituals and ceremonies—with elaborate etiquette and protocol for hospitality, generosity, etc. Eating becomes increasingly a fulfillment, not just of biological hunger, but of personal appetite regulated by social convention, of symbolic goals and purposes, of emotional expressions.

Elimination is an organic need that must be met throughout life. But elimination becomes regulated, patterned, governed by social requirements, often deferred. It may be a vehicle for expression of dependence, of hostility, of anxiety, a ritual for cleanliness and modesty, of privacy, of shame.

Sleep likewise has been regulated by social requirements and patterned into group or individual rituals so that the organic need for recovery from fatigue is overlaid and subordinated to nonorganic and symbolic purposes and deferred goals, or as an escape.

Sex, as an organic capacity and physiological process, develops in adolescence with the maturation of the gonads. At this time the early tactual sensitivity is revived and reinforced by special sensitivity in the erogenous zones, and sex and tactual sensitivity become merged. Sex as a process may be transformed into a variety of vicariates and surrogates, of deferred and symbolic fulfillments into which the specific genital functions are patterned and channeled. Sex in our culture has been transformed into an interpersonal love relationship governed by the personality of the participants who use sexual functions and relationships, not primarily for procreation, but for all the

varied nonsexual goals and symbolic fulfillment they have
learned to seek.

Thus we see how these basic organic needs and functional
processes must continue throughout most of life and be satisfied
to some extent as essential to organic existence, but they are
usually regulated, patterned, transformed into goal-seeking,
purposive conduct addressed to deferred goals, greatly altered
consummation and fulfillments, often purely symbolic and yet
of overwhelming value to individuals. This is the unique capacity of the human, to exist as an organism, to carry on and
satisfy his organic functions but to utilize them for human
living, for values and for human relations, especially the interpersonal relationships in and through which these goals and
values are maintained.

In the same way man has patterned and invested his own
body and physiological processes with meaning and value, he
has also created his ideas of beauty and significance and imposed them upon nature. Thus each culture has, as it were,
developed its own designs or compositions, through which it
has seen the geographical environment in a highly selective
vision, with the feelings it has established as appropriate to such
a setting. Each culture has its own patterns and enjoyment of
the arts and of nature. Like culture, art organizes, rearranges,
patterns, adorns, selectively emphasizing and rejecting different
features and aspects of life. Thereby the arts have made man's
life more interesting and significant, helped man to find enjoyment and to delight in beauty. Indeed we may say that everything man has prized and admired has been given value and
meaning by the artists who have revealed or created that source
of esthetic experience.

Each cultural group has established its preferred patterns
not only for its activities but also for its thinking. Thus in each
culture there is a more or less standardized way of thinking and
reasoning, using certain ideas and relationships and criteria of

credibility as axiomatic, to be accepted without questioning. This accepted way of thinking, the *eidos* of the group, permeates and organizes the language and all the reflection and artistic creations of the people, giving all their speech and activities a coherence and underlying similarity and unity of meanings and relationships. Everything that happens is interpreted in terms of this basic way of thinking, of seeing relationships and finding meanings, of explaining and justifying events. Thus the religious beliefs and ceremonies, the techniques of hunting, agriculture and domestic arts, the care of the sick, indeed the whole complex of group sanctioned activities, will express in diverse ways the underlying *eidos* of the group.

Likewise, each group has established its approved ways of feeling, with conventional forms of expressing such feelings upon all recognized occasions, especially vital events like birth and death. Everyone in the group learns to respond and to show his feelings in the prescribed formal patterns, expressing grief or sorrow, joy or happiness, elation or depression, or other feelings as and when conventionally appropriate. The *ethos* of a group is of large significance because these patterns guide and control the sensibilities of the people, whether they will feel anything or be unmoved and indifferent, and in what way they will feel or express those feelings. According to their customary *ethos,* people will be sympathetic and compassionate or they will be aloof and harsh toward others; they will impute value and worth to plants, animals or certain individuals and deny it to others.

Just because a culture is a selective version of nature and human nature and is maintained by this patterned way of thinking and feeling, the *eidos* and *ethos* of the group offer the major clues to an understanding of a culture. The clearest expression of the *eidos* and *ethos* of a group is usually found in their arts wherein they combine both their ideas and feelings in a symbolic synthesis.

In each culture we find individuals engaged in a great variety of activities which are more or less incomprehensible to an outsider. Thus different sounds are used to designate what are the equivalents of familiar objects or actions. When the English say bread, the French say *pain*, the Germans *brot*, the Italians say *pane*, the Spanish *pan*, and so on, to indicate much the same kind of foodstuff made from almost identical materials by the same process of baking, sometimes in different shapes.

Different groups use different objects—some metal stamped with special designs, some paper with printed or engraved designs, some shells or beads or other articles—each giving a symbolic meaning and value to its chosen objects, used for what we call money, with different meaning in each group.

Likewise, each group has established its preferred practices for regulating human relations and meeting life situations—its ceremonies and rituals for courtship, betrothal and marriage, for childbirth, for entering adolescence, for becoming an adult, for death and burial.

What must be emphasized again and again is that each cultural group, in accordance with its four basic conceptions, has fitted the world and man into the patterns developed from these fundamental assumptions. The same, basically similar geographical environment of the earth and the same internal environment of human organisms have been selectively patterned and utilized for each of these cultural worlds.

Thus each cultural world is not a superhuman or supernatural creation nor even a separate and different environment; it is one of the dimensions of the environment, one of the many possibilities selectively formulated by man himself and tolerated, so to speak, by nature. Man himself puts forms, meanings and boundaries upon nature and lives within those self-imposed limits.

Each cultural world, therefore, may be regarded as a sort of shelter, like a house, which is constructed from materials taken from the environment to protect the occupants from certain impacts of the environment, cold or heat, rain or snow; other organisms, and to admit other aspects—air, light, fuel and also foodstuffs which can be stored and used when needed. Within the house a more or less orderly way of living becomes possible, with sustained relationships among individuals, with ceremonies and rituals and other patterns of interrelated activities.

In much the same way the cultural environment constructed by man is interposed between man and nature and his internal mammalian environment, so that only what each group selectively approves is accepted, all else being prohibited or rejected, ignored or warded off. Again, it must be repeated that each group has utilized the local geographical world, with its landscape, topography and indigenous plants and animals in creating their cultural and social environments. This gives a clue to the materials they have used, the role of particular plants and animals and the specific configuration employed in their *eidos* and *ethos* which often reflect local environmental aspects and processes. Thus the people who live in the jungle, or on an island, or in the arctic region, have incorporated these local situations and occupants into their cultural patterns.

The way this cultural environment arises and is maintained, the way it operates, gives further understanding of its organization and functioning. While no one can say how these patterns originally started, it is clear that once they were begun, even in a rudimentary fashion, they were perpetuated by being transmitted to each succeeding generation of children, as we can see today. In this process of transmitting traditions, we see something that may be called social inheritance, often as coercive as physical inheritance.

The newborn infant, being helpless and dependent and having a prolonged period of infancy, undergoes several years of growth and development when he is directly under parental care and direction. He is, therefore, more or less plastic and formative in his early years and again during the period of adolescence when he undergoes a further period of growth, development and maturation, of being again more or less flexible and plastic.

During his first early years the infant is progressively inducted into the cultural world of his family's traditions by a series of stages which increasingly shape, mould and direct him into the kind of organism-personality prepared to live in that cultural world.

Thus in the beginning of life the infant's internal environment, his mammalian functions, are systematically regulated and patterned. His biological hunger is sooner or later transformed into appetite for the kind of food his parents provide and consume for their own nutrition, eaten at the intervals they have set for meals—once, twice, three times or more a day—or eating when food is available. Under this parental care and feeding, the child adjusts his physiological functions to the prescribed patterns of nutrition, learning how to utilize his reserves to carry him over the intervals between eating.

He also learns to manage his bodily elimination according to whatever patterns are established for urination and defecation. The child is required sooner or later to learn how to retain urine and faeces until he can go to the designated place for evacuation. Along with this control the child may learn various prescribed practices of personal cleanliness, of privacy, of modesty, and so on as transformations of the functional process of elimination.

It is important to recognize that in these early lessons the infant is required to surrender some of his own physiological autonomy or internal self-regulation of his nutritional and eliminative functions. Thereby his internal environment is brought under social control.

Sooner or later the infant or young child is also restricted in the expression of his emotional reactions. He may be permitted to react with anger or rage or fear whenever provoked, or expected to accept such provocations, especially when being denied, without being emotionally disturbed or at least without showing such emotions.

Through regulation of feeding and elimination and emotional reactions, the individual is to a greater or lesser extent freed from insistent hunger, from spontaneous elimination, from strong impulses, and so is enabled to do many things which would be difficult, if not impossible, without this freedom from the coercion of his organic requirements. By these same processes his functional needs are transformed into wants, desires, deferred goals and consummations to which the individual is increasingly oriented. He learns to seek fulfillment of his organic needs as they have been culturally transformed into purposive activities and human relations.

When the young child begins to move about and explore the world, he meets with various interferences, with mother's hand and voice blocking him, slapping him, prohibiting him from going to certain places, from touching or taking or eating what is forbidden, and otherwise frustrating his spontaneous, impulsive activities. These prohibitions operate to protect him from real or supposed dangers and to curb him from doing what is not allowed.

By being repeatedly deprived and frustrated, he gradually learns to refrain from approaching or touching what is forbidden and so slowly he builds up the general pattern of inviolability of things or people. This is strengthened by the love and approval of adults. Thus he learns to respect what we call the private property of things, the sacredness of places, and the bodily integrity of others.

Each cultural world defines what is to be left untouched in different terms, according to its traditions, but the same basic process of child rearing operates, of denying approach to what is forbidden until the child learns to accept the restrictions upon his activity. The way these prohibitions are enforced and the time they are imposed differs, however, as do the punishments given for failure to observe these prohibitions. The child, under all these different practices, is expected to accept the prohibitions and transform them into self-administered inhibitions, thus taking over the cultural patterns and enforcing them upon himself.

In each cultural world there are also many prescribed patterns which the young child is required to learn and to exhibit in his various activities. He must learn the required practices of personal cleanliness and grooming, of formal manners and etiquette, especially in eating, in greeting or responding to others, the first steps in the masculine and feminine roles, the prescribed conduct of interpersonal and group activities. Here, again, these requirements will be differently phrased and expressed in each group, but they are imposed upon the growing child to guide and direct his naive behavior into the orderly patterns approved by his family and his social life, often highly specialized according to age, sex, kinship, social status, and so on, of each individual.

Just as the child surrenders much of his physiological autonomy and learns to function as required, so the child also gives up his naive, direct relation to the environment, transforming his impulsive behavior into purposeful conduct toward the cultural world as presented by his parents.

The growing child is also introduced to language, usually learning to recognize and respond to words and then developing speech himself. Thus, he learns that everything has a name and a meaning, defined in terms of what it does or what must be done to or for it and its relation to other objects, persons or events.

If he asks questions about things or events and wants to know the why of things, he is told by parents what the traditional beliefs and assumptions offer as reasons or sanctions or explanations of how things operate. In this way the child is inducted into the cultural world of beliefs and assumptions, and of selective awareness, the group-approved ways of thinking, believing and feeling about the world and other people and himself. He is taught, more or less formally and systematically, the four basic conceptions of his cultural world as the only right, proper and permitted way to look at the world, to understand its makeup and operation and to think about himself and his conduct.

By these successive lessons the child learns to live in a world defined or translated by parents and others according to traditions, to accept these definitions and to impose them upon the environment and human beings, thereby creating and maintaining the cultural world. The actual world of events becomes invested with the meanings and significances disclosed by tradition, just as the child becomes patterned in his thinking, acting and feeling to live according to those defined meanings and significances.

Human behavior becomes transformed into patterned conduct which approaches the environment in these selective purposeful ways and thereby transforms it into the cultural world. Insofar as the environment performs according to these assumptions, conforms to the beliefs and expectations of the traditional formulations, it gives validity to these traditions and permits man to carry on his preferred way of living.

It is as if each child, during his helpless and credulous infancy and early childhood, were hypnotized and told that for the rest of his life he would always see the world, think about it, approach and utilize it and also conduct his life, including his human relations, according to the suggestions or definitions of the hypnotist. Each child growing up in a cultural world does just that and so he becomes an active member of his cultural world, taking over and perpetuating its traditions more or less faithfully.

But, as we will discuss in a later chapter, in each culture what the individual child learns may differ to a greater or less extent from the "pure" or formal tradition as translated by adults, and so he develops his own private, personal version of the prescribed patterns of action, speech, belief and feelings. He becomes more or less individualized.

If we will reflect upon this situation, we will, as pointed out in the beginning of this chapter, begin to realize how remarkable is the situation presented, of man, essentially alike, existing in the same geographical environment, but living in his different cultural worlds, cherishing his traditions and transmitting them to the next generation, thereby maintaining this cultural world as a highly selected patterned version or dimension of the environment.

In this process we may observe something very similar to what occurs in the internal environment. As described in the preceding chapter, the cells of the organism are being continuously worn out, discarded and replaced by new cells, the chemical constituents of the organism are constantly being replaced by new chemical atoms, but the specialized organs, tissue and functions go on operating in their specialized but coordinated patterns. The whole organism continues to exist in its usual shape or configuration, gradually altering in size and weight and functional efficiency with the passage of time.

In much the same way we may see the cultural traditions and these specialized patterns being perpetuated over the years, while the individual members of the group die and are replaced by new individuals who are fitted into these patterns, thus carrying on or perpetuating tradition.

Moreover, as we will discuss in the next chapter, each cultural group has established a social order, a more or less highly organized way of group living, with institutions and formal arrangements and relations, governed by these basic beliefs and assumptions which are maintained and carried on by succeeding generations, which take over and learn to live within these social patterns.

This reinforces the earlier statements about the kind of world we live in—a world which persists by an unending process of dynamic change, with nothing fixed and stable except the patterns, the configurations, the organizations which are maintained by the changing constituent parts or members who by their way of acting create and perpetuate these patterns and organizations.

It is indeed amazing to realize that what endures in the world are these intangible but potent configurations, these patterns and organizations that arise and operate only as relationships, dynamic actions, reactions and interactions of "transactions" among the innumerable constituents.

And out of this incessant activity and never ending change comes order, regularity, even fixity and rigidity as we see in the various organisms which are so resistant to alteration and in man's traditions and institutions which are likewise resistant to modification.

But the cultural environment can and does change, as the history of mankind indicates. If we look back into the dim past as nearly as we can now reconstruct it, early man appears quite different from today except in some of the smaller cultures where apparently the early patterns of culture have persisted from the Stone Age.

The early man who lived in caves, fought with crude weapons and used simple stone knives and axes, apparently had fire and, in some groups, made pottery, baskets and tools and ever more effective weapons. Some of these early men developed ceremonies and rituals, as indicated by archeological findings. And they domesticated plants and animals.

While he was often faced with a precarious world and compelled to exert his major efforts in getting food and protecting himself and his dependents, it seems clear that early man already was engaged in culture building, was developing ideas as well as tools, formulating, however crudely, the four basic assumptions to guide his activities and way of living.

Early in his history, as if bored with what nature offered, or as a magical way of trying to control nature, he began to create his arts, to design and color and compose, to draw and paint and sculpture, on walls of caves, on skins of animals, using wood, clay, stone and bone, ornamenting his weapons and tools and his own body, often with symbols, very complex designs and representations. He also began to manipulate and deform parts of his own body—nose, lips, ears, teeth, feet, and his own skull and genitals.

The environment and his own organism were the raw materials for his imagination to shape and manipulate, always emphasizing in his artistic work whatever was considered to be important and minimizing or eliminating the rest, thereby producing something that was a selective version, a transformation of what existed.

Likewise, early man began to develop what we now call music, rhythmic sounds, with his own voice and then instruments, like drums, and dances in which he rehearsed what had happened to him or what he hoped would occur, as in rituals to influence the weather, and fertility, or to release and express his feelings.

Also he began to tell himself stories, expressing his hopes and fears, or explaining in terms of his basic assumptions the nature of things.

In all his artistic endeavors early man was engaged in the same basic activities of culture building, of selecting from the environment and from his own potentialities what he would pay attention to, cultivate, elaborate and utilize in his cultural world. Thus we may say that culture is essentially an artistic achievement, an attempt by man to create a human world, at once natural but with all the elements differently arranged and organized, with the meanings and values imposed upon events, according to their basic assumptions about nature and man, always directed by the feelings which so largely control human life.

Language is essentially an artistic creation, a variety of auditory and written symbols, of metaphors and similes or other figures of speech with which we can organize or describe our experiences, and communicate because those symbols arranged in a certain order and sequence will evoke from others similar ideas and feelings, stimulate responses to us or to others as the language symbols, with their rhythms, their cadence or the tone of voice which utters them, arouses others to action and to feelings.

Figures, arithmetic and mathematics, are also symbols for communication and for ordering (measuring) observations, experience, and especially events, with which, as in engineering, we want to deal purposefully.

In all societies, but more clearly exhibited in those with a written language, the language has form, systematic structure and approved ways of being used such as we see in grammar, rhetoric, and the more precise rules of semantics. In these established patterns of language the "psycho-logic" or *eidos* of the culture—its basic preconceptions and criteria of credibility—govern the use of words.

Likewise in its mathematics are expressed its conception of possible orders of events and relationships so that mathematics serves as a systematic and more precise way of interpreting experience and of putting meaning into the world, the underlying process of all culture, but in mathematics refined, controlled, critically checked for internal coherence and credibility and neutrality of symbols.

Each speaker and writer, moreover, however illiterate and crude his expression, is essentially an artist, seeking by verbal or written symbols, by figures of speech to create a picture, a communication that will have meaning for another as he uses these traditional patterns of language. In this manipulation of symbols which we use to impose meaning upon events and people, and as surrogates for whatever is symbolized, we are daily and hourly rehearsing the basic process of culture formation and maintenance. Only as we continue to think (that is talk to ourselves) and speak and act in accordance with the symbols and meanings of our group life, to invest every object and animal and every situation with its traditional significance do we have a culture and enjoy the order and the security which a culture gives us.

Thus we can say that every culture is a great human achievement in its basic beliefs and assumptions, but a culture is essentially that which is sought (as Ortega Y. Gasset has said). Thus every culture is an aspiration, an endeavor toward a chosen way of life, based upon the traditional meanings and the processes of valuing which each group of people cherish as *the* way.

Man is apparently the only organism which has developed this capacity for investing situations and people with symbolic meanings and values, finding in life opportunities for creating designs for living which can yield enjoyment, delight, with goals and the values he cherishes.

It is significant that every culture arose in the dim past when early man had no guide to the understanding of nature and himself beyond his direct observation of events and his imagination and feelings.

The varieties of culture, therefore, represent an extraordinary achievement in creating assumptions and conceptions of nature and of man which made life orderly and meaningful.

But, as we are now discovering, these basic assumptions and beliefs are all pre-scientific; they reflect and express how early man saw the world and how he tried to explain its creation, operation and meaning. They are in large part the product of his fantasy and intuitive feelings about natural events, which he usually explained as if they were the acts and purposes of another, but larger, more powerful man. Thus, many of the cultures see the world and all its activities in terms of hidden but powerful spirits or deities controlling all events.

Mingled with many of his careful and shrewd observations upon actual processes were these basic assumptions that explained all occurrences in terms of occult forces and the motives and intents of the presiding deities or supernatural spirits. The variety of these supernatural powers and their ways of operating is amazing indeed, testifying to man's extraordinary ingenuity and imagination. But the cultures which were developed and established upon these assumptions are, as we can now see, archaic survivals in a world where scientific investigation is beginning to provide ever more dependable knowledge and understanding about nature and man.

As we discover more clearly the order of events and begin to understand the kind of universe we live in, all of these cultural worlds have become obsolete and incredible in their underlying beliefs and assumptions. Thus, we are today witnessing the accelerated breakdown all over the world of the historically developed traditions by and for which people have lived and reared their children, each group confident that it had the right and final answer to all man's basic questions. Yet in all these cultures, as in our own, there are amazing discrepancies and irreconcilable conflicts as in our religious beliefs.

Some cultures have existed unchanged, except for minor variations, from the remotest ages. Our Western European culture has, however, been in process of change for many, many centuries, as we are discovering among the ruins of the earliest groups in the Middle East, Babylon, Assyria, Persia, India, Egypt, and from the surviving monuments and records of the Semitic peoples. There has been a succession of peoples with different cultures which have risen and flourished for a while and then crumbled and passed, leaving only the ruins of once mighty temples and tombs, of large cities or occasionally a record carved in stone or preserved on some kind of material that has outlasted the centuries. Many of their ideas, symbols and ceremonies, however, have survived, to be adapted and incorporated in other cultures.

From the time of recorded history in Greece, we can trace the successive changes that have occurred in the basic conceptions of their culture, how in Greece in the sixth and fifth centuries, B.C., critical thinking became organized into a systematic examination of tradition, a critical questioning of religion and philosophy and custom, a search for new ideas and patterns of conduct.

Later we can read of how Copernicus, Gallileo and Kepler, Newton and their many successors developed new conceptions, new ways of understanding nature and, more recently, how we have developed new ideas about man, his origin and his human nature.

Today we are beginning to realize that as a people we are undergoing the most far-reaching and disturbing changes in all our cultural traditions. There have been several revolutions in our tools and technology in the past. Today scientific research, bringing new knowledge of how basic processes operate and how the atom can be manipulated to release its potential energy, forecasts not only further changes in our technology but also a recasting of almost all of the traditional ideas and beliefs about the universe and the order of events.

We are, therefore, faced with the necessity of having to accept change in our culture, to recognize that we can and must revise and replace our historically developed traditions in order to meet the persistent tasks of life more effectively. If we can see these impending changes, not as the end of all things, as many are fearfully thinking, but as the continuation of the historic process of creating and developing a human way of life, then we can critically examine all our traditions and begin to create the new patterns to replace those that have become obsolete and anachronistic.

For the revision of our *eidos,* or system of thinking, we have the belief in man's own capacity to build a human world and the findings of scientific research telling us how the universe is constituted and how it operates, so that we can rebuild our cultural world by replacing these now obsolete ideas and assumptions with new, more credible and productive concepts. Thus we can build up a new set of assumptions and a wholly new way of thinking which will be logical because it will guide our use of words or terms and our statement of relations by the observed and verified processes of nature.

The traditional *eidos* of every group will require alteration to bring their ways of thinking into harmony with the new understanding of the order of events as now being revealed. Some cultures will be more nearly in accord with the recently developed dynamic circular conception of the universe than others which, like our own, have long been guided by mechanistic conceptions and linear assumptions. Some of man's intuitive understanding of the world finds a formal expression today in recent scientific concepts, but this is limited to the conceptions of a few minor cultures. Western man has been peculiarly biased toward static concepts and mechanistic ways of thinking about the world and man, viewed as rigid and fixed. These assumptions are now revealed as irreconcilable with the actual dynamic circular processes of nature. Thus we have an enormous task of revision of our historic culture involving a reorientation of many of our basic patterns of thinking and reasoning and a critical revision of most of our symbols, especially our language.

Every aspect and element in culture, predicated upon assumptions about the universe and how it operates, including man and his functioning, will require critical examination in the light of recent scientific advances. Since the ongoing march of scientific research will continue to bring new knowledge and understanding, this process of revision must go on indefinitely. Today almost every personality is torn by conflict and faced with confusion, trying to reconcile these conflicting beliefs of our traditions that have become archaic.

For the revision of our *ethos,* or conventional ways of feeling, we have as guides the belief in the value and worth of the individual and the aspiration toward the dignity of man. To these we can add the growing understanding of and ever more penetrating insights into human nature and personality, giving us a clearer realization of the role of emotions and feelings, of how they are frequently warped and twisted and disturbed by our cultural traditions and customary ways of rearing children. Today we can and must give up the traditional attitudes of regarding man's emotions as the source of evil, of sinfulness and disorder, and begin to recognize that man must always be guided by his feelings which, however, as cultural history shows, can be focused and redirected into new patterns.

We need an *ethos* of sensibilities and feelings which will reinforce and serve the values of our tradition which so often have been defeated, if not destroyed, by the archaic ideas derived from the past, and the conflicting and destructive feelings these have fostered in the growing child.

A new *eidos* and *ethos* will provide the dimensions for reconstructing our social environment.

V

The Social Environment
of Group Living

Just as groups of people all over the earth have developed their cultures as a human way of living in the geographical environment, a man-made creation imposed upon nature and human nature, so each cultural group has developed its own social order or way of living together.

Every social order, of which there are many different kinds, is an expression and an application in human conduct of the basic underlying cultural assumptions and beliefs, the *eidos* and the *ethos* described in the preceding chapter, translated into more or less rigidly prescribed patterns, rituals and practices of conduct, especially in the interpersonal relationships and varied activities among people.

Each social order has developed over the centuries, guided by these underlying assumptions and beliefs, but the actual institutions and practices, such as the political, economic, legal and social arrangements and relationships, have grown without plan, purpose or foresight in most societies. The existing conditions in a society are usually regarded by the members as inevitable and unchangeable and are explained and justified by the traditional beliefs of the group, even when they know that these institutions have been established recently, as in our own society.

Just as a culture arises and is maintained by being incorporated into the growing child who learns to see the world, to think, to act, to feel as he has been taught, so in the same way social order is maintained and operated by a similar translation of group patterns, practices, symbols, into the activities and conduct of every individual member of the social group.

As the infant and young child is culturized, he learns to speak and understand language, he learns to live in the world of meanings and values communicated to him by language and reinforced by the learned conduct of respect for things, places and persons, and of performance of the various prescribed formalities and roles.

The child grows up in a well defined cultural environment wherein everything and every person and every event has been named and explained and defined and made the occasion for the required conduct, of avoidance or of performance. Thus, he learns to live in this cultural world and to believe what is dictated by his family's religion, philosophy, law and custom as true and dependable and, what is important, with penalties for failure to follow the prescribed rules and sometimes for even questioning them.

As the child grows older he takes over these traditions and accepts these prescriptions, incorporates them into himself, in-

hibiting the impulses that would lead to violation of the prohibited actions, compelling himself to perform the many formalities and the duties expected of him and otherwise fitting
himself into the cultural environment.

He, therefore, finds himself in the geographical environment of space and time, of plants and animals, of objects and of
people, each of which, however, has its meaning and for each
its appropriate mode of approach or of being left alone. While
many places, objects, people are physically accessible, can be
entered, touched, taken, used or directly approached, they may
be inviolable, not be entered, touched or approached as
demonstrated to the child by repeated experiences of being
stopped and denied in early childhood. Certain places, things
and people must be treated in a special manner, with the formalities that were taught him when he was told to perform
these prescribed actions.

Thus the growing child, after being trained to observe
these prohibitions and prescriptions, is further inducted into
the group life by learning to use the appropriate rituals, formal
patterns and associated symbols in all his activities. Blocked in
any direct approach to things or persons, he learns how to nego-
tiate for things, by dealing with the owner in accordance with
the socially sanctioned practices of barter or sale, or other interpersonal agreements regarding objects and animals. Likewise,
he learns to make agreements with others for their services or
the temporary use of their tools, goods, land or houses. Also, he
learns the prescribed rituals and symbols for each kind of interpersonal relationship, including courtship and betrothal and
marriage, with whatever ceremonies and arrangements they
involve.

Through a series of such teachings the individual, as he
grows up, becomes familiar with, and more or less skillful in,
utilizing the established practices for living in the group where,

apart from such technical activities as are addressed only to plants, animals and objects, almost all of his daily living is concerned with interpersonal relationships.

It must be emphasized that group living is primarily focused in and upon activities wherein one person deals with another or a group of other individuals, utilizing the socially prescribed patterns for such conduct. Thus if a group has individual private property in things and animals, which are inviolable to others, anyone desiring those things or animals, deals not with the thing or animal but with the owner; to the owner he must make an offer of something or a promise to do or give something in the future as a way of persuading the owner to release the thing or property. Having agreed to sell or barter the property to another, the original owner then must transfer it and refrain in the future from approaching or taking or using what he has conveyed to another.

Each group has worked out its own more or less elaborate rules and regulations for these transactions between and among individuals, each of whom must observe all the prescribed formalities and often openly and publicly declare their intentions, as in transfer of property. Indeed, for the conveyance of land and animals and other property, there may be an elaborate code of procedures, with formal written documents in literate groups to record the transfer of ownership and establish what the lawyers call the title.

Even the more simple cultures, that is, those with only a few tools and techniques and relatively little of goods compared with our industrial society, may have very complicated practices for changing ownership, involving ceremonies and religious rituals and priestly sanctions, just as in our society individuals are required to acknowledge publicly their signature on a document, appearing before a notary and taking the oath to give their declaration the necessary validity and credibility.

An even more complicated set of practices may govern the

relations of individuals to each other wherein one agrees to perform certain services for another, as we see in employment. Sexual relations between a man and a woman are usually governed by an elaborate code, especially in those societies where marriage is involved in a complicated web of family, property, and other arrangements calling for prolonged negotiations, or for bride price to be paid the bride's father or brothers, or dowry to be given to the husband, or premarital agreements when required to insure the inheritance of property, the education and control of the children, and similar arrangements.

In general it may be said that each group has developed more or less rigidly defined patterns to regulate every socially recognized form of interpersonal relationship. These are established and maintained according to the basic cultural traditions and derive their sanctions from the religion, philosophy and law of the group and are enforced by whatever authority or power the group recognizes as controlling, as in the use of the oath.

In most societies there is a variety of restrictions and privileges which apply to certain designated individuals and limit what they can do as contrasted with others or confer upon them special permission to do what others are not allowed to do or even make it mandatory for them to do.

Each member of a society, therefore, has a status, defined in terms of what he can and cannot, may and must do, his rights and duties. These vary according to various criteria—age, for example, operates to change the individual's status, especially as seen in the restrictions and privileges of children of different ages. Likewise, sex defines the status of individuals since males and females usually have different rights and duties, the female often being limited in her rights and the exercise of various practices, or compelled to perform certain services as a female.

Membership in a certain family or kinship group, especially when that group has certain hereditary privileges, may give an individual a special status which may be graded according to a hierarchy of nobility, of color, of size, of land or cattle ownership, with recognized signs or symbols of distinction.

Among these special privileges are the right to govern others, to exercise authority and use compulsion to make others obey the governing individual's or group's commands. Thus there may be a small group or family with control over large numbers of individuals of subordinate status who must serve their superiors, as in slavery, serfdom tenancy and other recognized forms of dominance and submission.

These distinctions may operate to prohibit marriage between an individual of one status and an individual of another status and yet not prevent extra-marital sex relationships. Indeed, in many societies the females of the group with lower status are frequently approached sexually by the males of the higher status group, the children of such unions, if any, usually taking the status of the mother.

Since in these many different interpersonal relations conflict and differences frequently arise, due to negligence or failure to carry out agreements, to deceit and fraud, to misrepresentation and other forms of deliberate or unintentional deficiencies in the goods, animals, services involved, there are established practices for settling such disputes, ranging from group sanctioned individual violence to elaborate rituals, such as our legal trials before a judge or jury. Here is found a web of elaborate rules and prescriptions, with various rituals for establishing the credibility of witnesses, such as our familiar testimony under oath or other tests of validity.

Then, also, there are in some societies formal patterns for members of the group of certain defined status (age, sex, and so forth) to participate in the determination of laws and group affairs. The variety of governments, as we call these arrangements for maintaining the social order and regulating its affairs, is almost endless, with the control limited to a small group or dispersed among a larger number of people.

It will be seen that the social environment is established by these many patterns and rituals, these formal arrangements and relationships which members of the group utilize in all their affairs.

The social environment is like the paths and roads and the fences or barriers and the buildings which are laid out and established upon the geographical environment to give it a certain fixed pattern and structure which those living in that area must observe in their movements. The paths or roads or streets become the socially approved routes to be travelled in going from one location to another, and the fences and barriers and buildings prevent most of the attempted deviations from these established paths. Once the members of the group have learned to travel in this way, their continued use of these paths establish them as *the* ways to move about and, therefore, they operate to guide, if not control, other activities until the whole group life has become firmly patterned upon these highways and buildings. Thus buildings of various kinds, houses, temples or churches and markets, arise in certain locations and become the focus of all the activities associated with the practices defined by those buildings. Once these patterns are established and become the customary way, they will tend to persist since the children grow up to use what their elders accept and use. Moreover, people get vested interest in such patterns and use and cling to their privileges, resisting any proposed change.

But the social environment is more than the layout of land and buildings and location of customary activities; it is essentially these intangible but coercive patterns and practices, these rituals and institutions of private property, of marriage and family life, of government, of law enforcement, of religious observances and all their associated practices and symbols like money and credit, etc. Like the cultural environment, the social environment is created and maintained by what members of the group have learned to believe, to do and not to do, and their more or less skillful use of the prescribed practices, use of symbols and rituals.

The social environment may be likened to an elaborate game in which the area of playing is carefully marked off as in a field with boundaries and goals or as in chess. There are rules and regulations for playing the game which everyone is expected to follow, although these rules are purely arbitrary conventions. Thus there is no physical barrier to a player's moving in any way he choses or going out of bounds or otherwise failing to keep his activities within the prescribed design and rules of the game. There is nothing to keep the chess player from moving his pieces in any direction he may wish except the self-accepted rules of the game and the requirement of his opponent for conformity to these conventions.

Just as man everywhere has created a cultural world to give meaning and significance to life, so he has established his various social orders which regulate his conduct and maintain the established rules and conventions. These operate to keep human activities and interpersonal relations within a definite prescribed framework, thereby making the otherwise disorderly and unpredicatable human behavior into a more or less orderly complex. Each member of the group, while pursuing his own purposes, utilizes the socially approved practices and observes the conventional patterns and rituals in whatever he may wish to do, especially in relation to others; thus he presents himself in familiar, understandable ways to others, His conduct, at least outwardly and formally, can be interpreted according to the conventions and met by an equally formal conventional response. Everyone knows what to expect and what is expected or required of him.

This serves to diminish the disruptive and conflict-breeding activities to a minimum because people know what can and cannot, may or must be done and how to meet these approaches by others, even though the individuals involved are concealing their feelings and their ulterior purposes. Deviations and violations of the social rules may occur without invalidating the group practices.

Human relations become a series of interpersonal situations in which individuals act, react and interact, guided by these established patterns and using the customary practices, rituals and symbols with their recognized meanings. Each individual enjoys both the advantages of these formal approaches and their protection, since the other individual must more or less faithfully conform to the conventions for which there is an established response.

What is of equal importance is that each individual, with his unique organism and life experience, with his mammalian functions and impulses, and his emotional reactions and feelings, finds in these socially sanctioned rules and practices an approved outlet or release for what otherwise might be forbidden or disturbing to others. Through these social patterns, individuals pursue goals and engage in purposeful conduct, thereby channeling their organic needs into socially acceptable activities and human relations. Often the individual may find these conventions are too restrictive or demanding and may conform only with difficulty or attempt to evade these requirements. Or he may openly repudiate them and act in antisocial ways which challenge law and custom and expose him to whatever penalties are imposed for such violation.

Just as the child slowly learns to live in a cultural world and accept the prescribed patterns of inviolability and of performance which restrict his impulsive behavior, so the growing individual gradually learns the rules and conventions of the social world. In the same way he takes these over, incorporates them into his own conduct, enforces them by his own self-discipline and lives according to what is permitted or required, sensitive to criticism or reproach or possible punishment for any failure of observance.

Each individual grows up in the social life to play his or her part, defined by the masculine or feminine roles which with greater or less difference prescribe the appropriate conduct for men and for women. Each one becomes a player in the elaborate social game in which he acts like a piece on a chessboard.

As is generally known in the game of chess, the various pieces, called pawns, knights, rooks, castles, kings and queens, are first arranged upon the board in a prescribed order, each piece having its conventional square. As the game is played, each piece according to its status has a definite range and direction of movement, with certain powers peculiar to each piece. Moreover, each piece is vulnerable in certain ways to attack and can also defend itself, according to its status.

In social life the individual likewise starts with a certain place, position and status according to his age, sex, kinship, and so on, and as he grows up these ordinarily change. But all through life he is at once an actor, approaching others according to his status and his desires, and also a recipient of action from others approaching him according to their status and desires. To some individuals he finds he has a limited approach or is forbidden to approach, as in sexual taboos, while to others he has the right or privilege of increasing freedom of approach even to the extent of exploiting, injuring and otherwise using the other. What he can or cannot do to or for or with another is governed by his status and the status of the other individual.

Likewise, each individual is open to approach from others to a greater or less degree depending upon his status and the status of the individual approaching. Toward some he may act to refuse or repel their approach, as an attempted invasion of his rights; towards others he must be submissive, allowing them to do to or for or with him (or her) whatever that individual may wish, without showing any resistance, as the child to his parents.

This relationship of dominance and submission, of using and being used, is the prevailing pattern in social life all over the world, although there are some societies which show little or no such patterns. Even in so-called enlightened societies, such as our own, women and children are expected to be submissive, accepting whatever treatment the dominant male may accord to the female or accepting whatever treatment the parent may give the child. Only recently have women begun to emerge from the many handicaps, limitations, legal and social restrictions and the unlimited power and authority of fathers and husbands, to enjoy any personal rights of inviolability and of personal integrity. Even today marriage among many involves wifely obedience and submission to the husband's desires, however unwelcome or abusive.

Again it must be emphasized that individuals accept their status, conform to these requirements and suffer these forms of exploitation and domination as necessary and unavoidable aspects of human life, especially since the basic beliefs and assumptions, the *eidos* of the group, as stated by the church and the government, reinforced by customs and public opinion, sanction these relationships. Indeed, it has been repeatedly shown that individuals who suffer from this exploitative treatment will actively resist any effort to free them or to modify their status. The prevailing patterns are so firmly established and so strongly reinforced by the individual's beliefs about the universe and man that he will regard any proposed alteration as impious.

Most of the betterment of human status that has been slowly achieved in different societies has come not by the protest or revolt of the exploited but by the efforts of a few superior or privileged individuals who have sought to modify the established laws and practices to help others of a lower status group.

The social environment, being familiar and often the only

possible arrangement known to a people, is believed to have been established by a higher power and usually seems to be wholly natural and inevitable.

There has been much questioning about the nature of social order, with many theories offered to explain how government, economics, social life generally is organized and how it operates. Most of these explanations are concerned with the particular kind of social order in which the writers have been reared and so they usually fail to give much light upon the social orders of other peoples with different cultures.

In our own traditions we find that social order has been explained at different times in various ways. The oldest and most venerable belief is that some time in the remote past social order was decreed by a supernatural power who issued his laws or commandments. Many other peoples have a similar belief that at one time their ancestors received a prescription for social order, a series of laws to be obeyed under penalty of awful punishment from on high. Such commandments or laws were beyond questioning and any suggestion that they were not sacrosanct was regarded as impious.

Social order according to this conviction is to be regarded as a way of living imposed upon a people by a power or authority above them, usually supernatural but sometimes a great man, the cultural hero, who in time of danger, confusion or turmoil, saved his people and gave them the basic rules for living as a group. Social order as thus conceived is maintained by pious devotion to the rules or laws and by scrupulously following the prescribed rituals and practices for all human conduct.

We can find such convictions in our own Judaic traditions, especially in what we call the Old Testament of the Bible, where it is stated that the basis of social order was established by God and set forth in the Ten Commandments.

It is to be noted that organized government in our own history was regarded as an expression of divine authority. Thus the kings, the emperors and other rulers were proclaimed as such by the priests who validated their power and authority as divinely sanctioned. Divine right of kings to rule over a people was accepted without question for centuries, just as earlier the local social order was maintained largely by the church.

When the belief in divine right began to be questioned and acceptance of social order as an expression of authority was challenged, the search for the basis of social order, and for some way of explaining and sanctioning a less autocratic government, turned to nature. Then it was asserted that there was a natural law governing all human affairs which provided the only true and reasonable basis of government and of group living.

The ideas of the universe formulated by Newton as an orderly arrangement of bodies which were governed by large scale forces, like gravitation, provided a model for the new theories of social order and of government. These ideas were very effective in attacking the older authoritarian government and providing for more participation by people in their own law making and its administration according to natural laws.

Thus social order was conceived as inherent in nature, a large scale mechanism or organization, located somewhere between the earth and sky, operating by large social forces. By studying these forces and learning to live according to the laws that governed their operation, it was believed that man could keep his social order going harmoniously, like the planets moving around the sun with their orderly relations.

During the eighteenth and nineteenth centuries most of our prevailing political, economic and social theories were formulated in terms of this basic Newtonian conception. Political and governmental affairs were seen as expressions of natural laws, as stated in our Declaration of Independence and our Constitution, as well as in the many histories and textbooks on government. Economic affairs also were viewed as governed by large scale economic forces and economic laws inherent in nature and, therefore, not to be disregarded or violated without peril to our economic welfare. Social life generally was also conceived as a vast organization, expressive of natural laws and forces, self-regulating and self-balancing, like economic affairs.

Despite the inability to locate or identify any such system or organization or mechanism, or to measure any such forces, scholars and statesmen and writers generally have accepted this conception and interpreted whatever happens as due to the operation of these forces or to a failure to obey these laws. This they can do by interpreting the recorded activities of members of the group, such as prices, wages, rents, votes, marriages and divorces etc., as actual entities changed by or as measurements of these supposed forces, ignoring the human origin of these activities and the use of these symbols and rituals.

No individual is ever in contact with these forces; he is exposed to the other individuals who make up his group and he experiences social order as it is constituted by other individuals using similar practices and rituals and symbols in their interpersonal relations.

Whatever happens to society has been regarded as the inevitable outcome of these underlying mechanisms and the expression of these forces which man was called upon to accept as controlling all events. This viewpoint or theory has fostered the belief in man's helplessness in the face of large natural forces which, like the movement of the planets, were far beyond any possibility of modification by any human effort. It has also fostered a feeling of irresponsibility for whatever happened in a society, no matter how it might violate the ideals of the group.

Not until fairly recently has it become evident that the specialized and rather peculiar kind of social order, with the kind of government, economic organization and activities and social life of Western peoples, was hard to explain as a part of nature when other people had such different forms of social order. If our kind of social order was natural and inevitable, governed by natural law and operated by natural forces, how could we explain these other and much older varieties of social order differently organized and operated? Moreover, how could we explain the historic record of large changes in social order from the Roman Empire, through the so-called modern society with the successive upheavals of the Agricultural Revolution in the middle of the eighteenth century, the Industrial Revolution of the nineteenth century, and the contemporary changes we are now witnessing?

The question many now are asking is how can there be so much order, regularity, almost uniformity in social life unless we invoke some higher power or authority or some large scale forces or natural laws, according to the concepts of the nineteenth century and earlier scientific thinking?

A promising answer to that question is in this conception of a social environment and of social order as man's own creation, the historically developed way of regulating human behavior and establishing and maintaining the kind of stable conduct necessary for group life.

If we took a visitor from a far off land, with no machines, and showed him our vast network of railways, with trains running on scheduled time, along fixed tracks, with regular stops and stations and all the elaborate apparatus of signals and train orders, of fast trains passing slow trains on sidings, and so on, he would probably consider this large, complicated and systematically operating arrangement to be a part of nature, run by invisible but potent forces, according to fixed immutable laws.

Since we know how the railroads were developed and gradually were extended and elaborated, we look upon them as man-made machines and a man-created and operated organization. But since we do not know how our social order started and we now find it operating in some mysterious way we cannot understand, we are inclined to follow the traditional belief that it originated from a supernatural source or came from nature.

Until recently scientific thinking conceived of orderly events as produced by the operation of large forces which moved particles and objects around in space. But more recently this conception has been superseded by another, of order and regularity arising from the ceaseless activity of energy transformations in a world of space-time which patterns and guides events according to the organization of space-time. This conception interprets the universe in terms of processes that operate in configurations or patterns which are more or less stable and persistent while the constituents are dynamically changing their positions, their velocity and their energy transformations.

This way of looking at nature may be applied to social life where we see many individuals acting, reacting and interacting, with greater or less intensity and rapidity, but following, more or less, the prescribed patterns of conduct, practices and rituals which thereby guide and channel their activities and so give rise to the appearance of order, regularity, almost uniformity.

Each individual member of a group, pursuing his own goals and purposes, but *using the prescribed rituals and symbols and practices in his individualized way,* by such activities within these patterns, creates and maintains the regularities of social order. The orderliness, the regularities and systematic appearance of society, are essentially the statistical uniformity of large numbers of individuals conforming more or less to the prescribed ways of acting, speaking and using prescribed patterns, although in some cultures each individual may be very faithful to the prescribed social patterns in a social life which offers or permits few deviations or alternatives. Social order differs from gas laws where innumerable disorderly molecules average out into recurrent regularities; the orderliness of group life arises from the learned patterns of conduct, especially of reciprocal interpersonal activities, using the rituals and symbols prescribed for social conduct and for the specialized activities. Thus social group living is like the organization of the human body described earlier as that which cells, tissues and organs maintain by their reciprocal interrelated but specialized functioning. Social order is like the team which is constituted by the patterned activities of the players.

It is evident that there can be a considerable range of individuality in what each member of a group desires or seeks, how he thinks, acts, speaks and behaves, but if he utilizes the established practices and conventions, and acts, reacts and interacts in these established patterns, as he must if his activities are to be understood and accepted by others, he will be maintaining the social order and everything he does will be systematically related to others' activities and to the over-all pattern and organization of the group life.

As pointed out earlier, organization is this interrelated, patterned activity of parts or members of a group or team. Social organization arises from the learned, patterned activity of the members of a group and is more or less self-perpetuating, like culture, because each generation of children grows up and learns to act like the parents and must follow these patterns.

This recent understanding of social order as that which is constituted by the patterned activities of many individuals offers a much needed conception to help us in reorganizing our social order. We are more or less frustrated, if not blocked by the belief that social order was imposed by a higher power, an authority who governed the social life and exercised control through a chief, king, emperor or other person of rank and power, or that social order was derived from natural laws and forces which man must obey and accept.

These long-accepted beliefs fostered a static attitude, a fatalistic view that whatever existed or happened was inevitable and unchangeable. But this older, unquestioning acceptance is disappearing as people no longer firmly believe in the assumptions which sanctioned the older state and social order.

By conceiving of social order as that which man creates and

maintains by his own patterned activities, we can begin to think of social order, not as something inexorably fixed by superhuman forces or supernatural powers which we must submissively accept, but as that which must be achieved and maintained by what man himself believes and does or refrains from doing.

What we call social problems are the persistent tasks of human living which came to each generation from its predecessors and their efforts to meet these persistent tasks. What each generation does to meet these tasks, modifying, changing, revising what was done before, will in turn give rise to the social problems of their successors. We cannot "solve" social problems, because they are expressions of the ways we face group living —they are produced by the very patterns and goals we seek. We can, however, reformulate our social problems in the light of new knowledge and understanding, of new tools and techniques and of new awareness and sensibilities. Social life thus appears as a human endeavor that must ever be problematic but which can be more flexible and adaptable as soon as we recognize social order as a human creation and a human responsibility.

This conception is peculiarly relevant to the situation that is developing all over the world where the historically developed social orders are breaking down. Revolutionary movements, challenging the old order, are appearing even in the most static and seemingly stable societies, just as they have become more frequent in our Western European societies.

The overthrow of ancient dynasties of kings and emperors who ruled with all the sanctions of the church to give their position and power a superhuman, if not supernatural, authority, indicates that the once unquestioned and unquestionable authority and social arrangements of dominance and submission have become intolerable.

What is to replace these older social orders has become the major issue in the world today. The conflict in each country is primarily between different conceptions of government, of group organization and operation, of individual status and participation, some clinging to the historic patterns, others advocating various modifications and changes designed to retain some of the old while accepting some newer patterns, and others boldly demanding a complete break with the past and establishment of a new social order.

The rise of totalitarian states and dictators, as exemplified clearly by Germany and Italy, but also in many other countries, reflects this breakdown of the old order with internal disorder and conflict, and the attempt to deal with the social situation on an ostensibly fiat basis of orders by the dictator. Behind the dictator are the smaller groups who are guiding and directing the program.

What should be realized is that all of these dictatorships *profess* a major concern for the welfare and happiness of the mass of people. The assertion of their aims and purposes to serve the good of the people, however false and misleading it may be, is of great significance as indicating that even a dictatorship feels the need to appeal to the good will of people for sanction and support. It is also significant that even a dictator, apparently able to exercise supreme authority and control over the whole life of a country, nevertheless looks to people for approval and does not attempt to invoke any of the historical sanctions, as did the autocratic kings.

Instead, dictators are invoking conceptions of manifest destiny, of inexorable trends and historical processes that can be accelerated or slowed down, but not changed. These and similar assumptions, like some of our social theories, imply that human conduct and group living are governed by coercive forces that must be submissively accepted and obeyed, always as interpreted by the dictator.

In every country all over the world, with greater or less rapidity, we can see the older ways of life being changed. In this process the new tools and techniques, the new machinery and equipment are modifying the older practices of industry, agriculture, mining and so on; in turn these new ways of making a living and of earning a living by gainful employment for money, are compelling people to change their living habits, their housing, transportation, communication, etc., but at the same time the subtle process of disintegration of their traditional beliefs about nature and social order are increasingly operating to modify and break down what people believe and expect.

Authority in its older form of power and orders or commandments, of expected obedience, is passing and the world is torn by conflicting beliefs about what should take its place and by the struggles of the older authoritarian organizations to retain their ancient power and control, or of new organizations seeking power over people and countries for their programs.

It is becoming clear that the rise of revolutionary groups, of subversive movements, and the growing disloyalty to established governments and institutions are indicative of a breakdown in the older ideas and beliefs, the former unquestioned loyalties that have become either meaningless or no longer acceptable.

As we look at the current scene and observe the confused activities of those who are attempting to direct our governmental and diplomatic affairs, our economic and other social activities, we see many individuals baffled by the situation they face. Few, if any, of the leaders have any understanding of what is happening or any clear idea about what they should do, except those who are striving to maintain the older arrangements against change. Our political and economic leaders are improvising from day to day, uncertain and anxious, often lacking any personal conviction of the formulas and slogans they continue to repeat.

This state of confusion reflects the widespread breakdown of the ideas and assumptions upon which social life has been based for so many centuries, and the lack of clearly defined alternatives to replace those which are passing. Until there appears a new formulation more in harmony with the emerging new conceptions of nature and of man, there will continue to be confusion and much conflict, because those who cling to the older practices will continue to oppose any change that threatens their privileges and power, and will justify their resistance by these obsolete ideas. Likewise those who are advocating authoritarian blueprints for the future of all societies justify their efforts by the ancient belief in human impotence and in the necessity of submitting to a superhuman historic process, proclaiming, as new and dynamic, the familiar old doctrines of human defeatism.

But everyone, radical, conservative and liberal-moderate, is a personality who pursues these different goals and strives for these divergent purposes that arise from his own private world. We cannot begin to deal with social situations effectively until we gain some understanding of these private worlds and how they arise and operate in human conduct.

VI

Our Private Worlds

As the preceding chapters have indicated, we exist as organisms in the geographical environment and also in the internal environment, our functional processes being maintained by continual intercourse and transactions between these two dimensions of the environment. We learn to live in the cultural and social environments by accepting the selective versions and symbolic interpretation of nature and man provided by tradition and by utilizing the customary patterns and practices of group life for conducting our interpersonal relations and carrying on our life careers.

The idea of man living in an environment with these four basic dimensions, so differently constituted by each cultural group, may at first appear almost too complicated to be grasped, but even this statement does not adequately cover man's multi-dimensional environment.

If we will look at human behavior more clearly and reflect upon the amazing diversity of individual conduct and feelings, the way each member of the group pursues his own peculiar goals and purposes and, in all of his actions, speech, beliefs and feelings, is so individualized, we must begin to realize that each of us actually lives as if in a "private world" of his own, within the life space he establishes for his personal living.

To understand these "private worlds" and how they arise, we must look again at the process of culturizing and socializing the child and observe how the individual personality emerges from the child's early life experiences.

But first it is necessary to point out that these "private worlds" are not subjective nor are they mysterious psychic structures apart from the rest of the environment. They are the life space which each individual builds up and maintains for himself by his selective awareness of, and idiomatic responses to, the several dimensions of the environment as he interprets them, with his peculiar, personal way of accepting and using the cultural and social environment for his individual needs, desires, functions and feelings.

We must remind ourselves again and again that we live in a world of many possibilities, that nature offers innumerable opportunities for the development of different designs for living, as we see in the great diversity of plants and animals which have evolved in the geographical environment and also as shown by the variety of cultural worlds which different groups have created and imposed upon nature and man.

Just as each culture is one of the many possible ways of conceiving the universe and man, one of the many potential patterns for organizing human experience, so each personality may be regarded as one of the almost unlimited ways in which each human organism can take over the traditional ideas and patterns of his group and translate them into a unique constellation, a wholly individualized personality.

Thus the conception of a "private world" and of a life space is but an extension of this process, operating all through nature, of selective awareness and utilization of the environment, which has produced the different complexes of energy we find in the various crystals, in plant and animal and in-between forms, and most recently, has appeared in that most plastic expression of nature, the human organism and the human personality.

If we will again look at the way the cultural environment is established and maintained by what is done to and for the infant and young child, we can gain insight into the emergence of personality and the rise of these "private worlds" in which each individual lives. For this understanding we are indebted to Sigmund Freud, who revealed the significance of early childhood experiences.

During the first year of life, as described earlier, the infant undergoes a series of experiences through which his internal environment is modified to meet the requirements and the specific treatment provided by his parents. Since the infant's internal environment is not yet stabilized, the individual organ system and functional processes are relatively flexible and plastic. He can, therefore, tolerate a wide variety of practices of infant care.

Thus the newborn infant within a short time after birth begins to become hungry. Before birth he has been continuously nourished within the mother who supplies needed foodstuffs. After birth he may be fed frequently or at long intervals and so must adjust his metabolic processes to whatever feeding practices his parents may favor.

As pointed out earlier, each infant has a unique heredity and arrives in the world with his individualized capacity to live and to adjust. Some infants have a rapid metabolism, use up their blood sugar rapidly and so become hungry at short intervals. Others have slower metabolism and do not become hungry as frequently, indeed, may exhibit little primitive hunger for food. Moreover, each infant will react to deprivation of food (being denied food when hungry or being interrupted when eating) in his own individual way: some babies show intense activity, quickly developing rage, while others show little or no restlessness when hungry and remain placid and undisturbed when their feeding is interrupted.

In being fed the infant gets more than food to allay his hunger; he receives comfort and relief from the bodily tensions that hunger increasingly creates throughout the organism (hunger itself starts as a series of rhythmic contractions in the walls of the stomach and as these become more intense, they spread and produce restlessness and often intense activity). Each time the young infant becomes hungry, he is in a state of acute disturbance. When this disturbance is allayed by food, he begins to expect such comfort from the world. With each experience of being comforted and relieved, his expectation grows and thereby he develops confidence in the world—a feeling of being cared for and protected.

Thus a dual process operates. His internal environment is kept stable and comfortable and the external environment, as it comes to him through parental care, becomes a source of gratification and fulfillment, a place to trust and rely upon. The infant does not reason this way, but *feels* this way and so reacts to the world as he feels.

If fed whenever hungry, he will gradually establish his own rhythm for eating and become more and more prepared to accept the daily schedule for eating as practiced by the parents. Thus he develops a persistent way of feeling about food, as a source of comfort and enjoyment, or, if he has been compelled to endure prolonged hunger, he may never develop a receptive attitude toward eating. Indeed eating may become a weapon to fight mother or to please her. Many of the so-called feeding problems begin in the early months when the infant experiences pain and frustration over food and so becomes resentful and antagonistic to eating.

Biological hunger, despite its basic role in organic living, can be and is subject to considerable modification, including many disturbances and distortions and, accordingly, it becomes transformed into the peculiar appetite for food which each individual exhibits.

The automatic elimination of urine and faeces when the contents of the bladder and bowel accumulate and thus release the sphincters is another biological process which undergoes modification and adjustment. In most societies some form of patterned elimination is required by the group, if only the simple act of eliminating outdoors. This calls for the development of some capacity to control elimination, learning to hold the sphincters closed until elimination can take place where required, and also to recognize preliminary bladder or rectal tension before actual elimination becomes necessary.

In the newborn infant elimination spontaneously takes place whenever necessary and the infant may not develop the capacity for control until a year or more later. Until then he needs to eliminate freely, without hindrance, so that this important function can operate without interference. If the parents try to train the child before he is ready, he may become tense and anxious, especially if they try to force him or punish him for failure to learn quickly.

Here again a basic biological process is modified and patterned to meet social requirements. The way this is done may develop a feeling of tension in the child. What should be a normal physiological function which regulates itself, subject to such later learned control as may be necessary for sanitation and cleanliness, may become an occasion for feelings that will continue and create various difficulties of elimination (such as persistent constipation or looseness of the bowels or a sensitivity to any stress or strain).

The infant has an all over tactual sensitivity, like other young mammals such as puppies, kittens, calves, etc., and apparently needs to be licked, nuzzled, cuddled, kept warm and soothed by close contact with the mother. This tactual sensitivity is especially acute in the genitals which later become the focus of adult mating. If the infant is mothered and given ample tactual contacts and soothing, he apparently will be more relaxed and function more effectively. Also he will develop the capacity for tactual contacts that will be renewed in adolescence for sexual relations.

The genitals of the infant are especially sensitive, and most babies in their exploration of their own bodies discover this and apply genital stimulation of one kind or another. If this infantile or early childhood genital manipulation is forbidden by the parents and punished, the child may become anxious about his genitals and by so much compromise his later sexual maturation. Also he may become guilty over any sex interests.

It is evident that the baby who is treated gently and protected from unnecessary discomfort, shock or pain, will feel secure and so will be able to live, stabilize his internal environment and grow without disturbance. Moreover, under such treatment the baby develops increasing confidence in the world.

It is important to recognize that this is a dual process, of progressive stabilization within the internal environment and of orientation to the external environment as a place to trust or to be fearful of; one facilitates and helps the other; a disturbance internally will compromise the external environment for the baby whose total organic reactions, inside and outside, govern his adjustment. Likewise shocks, pressures, punishment from outside will disturb the baby's internal environment.

In his development the child surrenders some of his own internal autonomy and accepts outside control or regulation of his organic functions. What is of greater significance is that the child gradually learns to defer satisfaction of his organic needs as he learns purposive conduct addressed to fulfillment of those organic needs but more importantly to the varied goals of his striving.

As pointed out in Chapter VI, the human infant has the unique capacity for utilizing and transforming his organic needs and functional processes into the culturally patterned, socially prescribed forms of purposive conduct and goal-seeking. The parents endeavor to guide or coerce the child into conformity to these established patterns, to accept this external regulation of his internal environment. But each child is a unique individual, with his or her inherited organism and potentialities which may be more or less amenable and responsive to this parental treatment.

How the baby feels inside, as a result of this early care and treatment, establishes his basic bodily state of ease and relaxation or of tension and discomfort, and so contributes to his image of his body. He enjoys living and finds fulfillment in eating, eliminating, in being loved and played with, or he finds living difficult and finds little or no gratification in these physiological functions. His internal functioning and feelings, to a greater or less extent, become invested in the life space he is organizing; thereby he perpetuates the situations in which he will continue to function and to feel in that way.

The emotional reactions of the infant are fully developed at birth and, as indicated, he meets every experience with greater or less physiological disturbance, such as acute emotional disturbances. How the child learns to curb or manage his emotional upheavals, especially when continually provoked, will vary according to the child and the way he is treated. Thus he begins to develop his own individual pattern of emotional reactions, to repress or to hold them in check as he learns to tolerate provocations without being disturbed, or to become persistently liable to be overwhelmed by rage or fear, often channeling these into various disguised expressions.

Each child, therefore, builds up his peculiar pattern of sensitivity and reactivity, of greater or less intensity, and establishes his own chronic feelings of anxiety, of guilt or resentment, of dependency and submissiveness, or of courage and confidence, of aloofness and suspicion or of love and affection and trust in people. This he does by establishing his life space with the meanings that evoke these responses.

When the child encounters the many denials and frustrations imposed by adults to establish respect for the inviolabilities of places, things and persons, he again learns to conform to these prohibitions but always in his own individualized way, with feelings that color and often distort the performance. Each child takes over these prohibitions in his own peculiar way and transforms them into self-administered inhibitions or repressions which express his pattern of acceptance of these social restrictions, sometimes with outright or partly concealed rejection and disguised evasions of these restrictions.

In the same individualized way the child learns to perform the various prescribed patterns of activity: personal grooming, manners and etiquette, masculine or feminine role, the conduct of his interpersonal relations. He accepts, learns, becomes skillful in some, or only partially accepts and never develops any skill or competence of performance in others. Moreover, depending upon how he was made to learn these practices, he builds up persistent ways of feeling which may be in conflict with the actions. Thus he may perform a prescribed action, but with such resentment against the authority that compelled him to learn that it is almost wholly ineffective, such as giving a required greeting in a surly, antagonistic way or doing what is expected of boys or girls with anxiety or resentment.

Each child develops a unique combination or pattern of performance, of inhibition or of action, for all these socially required practices, with feelings that become his characteristic way of living in the cultural and social world. He transforms his naive, impulsive behavior into patterned conduct as required for social life as defined by his parents but interpreted idiomatically himself.

When the child begins to use language he again learns to speak in a highly individualized way. He may learn to respond to words in his own way and to use words and phrases and sentences, with intonations and placing of emphasis, which are idiomatic—his own peculiar mode of interpretation and expression, of attempted communication. In this use of language this process of individuation is clearly shown and illustrated.

While there may be a more or less systematically organized official language with a recognized vocabulary and established definitions for each word, a grammar of correct usage, a rhetoric, all the apparatus of formal language, yet each individual speaks and writes in his own personalized way—his handwriting is peculiarly his own, his choice of words, his sentences, his mode of expression, all are characteristic of the individual but, nevertheless, are variations and combinations of the formal body of language symbols.

When the child is inducted into the customary ideas and traditional beliefs of his culture, this process of individuation in acceptance, understanding and use is again operative.

The parents will, according to their background of experience, cherish a somewhat warped and often inadequate version of the ideas, the beliefs, the assumptions more formally and precisely expressed in religious creeds, in philosophical formulations, in legal prescriptions and other socially recognized statements. This parental version may be expressive of various social, economic, political, sectarian and other variations within the cultural group, further modified by the parental intelligence and understanding and especially by their own childhood experiences.

What the parents teach the child as the correct, truthful

statement of the basic cultural conceptions may be, and usually is, their personal interpretation of the official formulations. Moreover, in teaching the child, often in times of stress and strain when the child is being admonished or punished or solemnly warned, the parents or other adults inevitably give their statements a special emphasis upon certain points or elements and infuse their teaching with their feeling toward that particular child at that moment.

It is clear that the child may receive, therefore, a curiously warped, often twisted and internally discordant statement of what he is to believe and to assume, of how he is to think about events, people and himself. All this content, especially of ethics and morals and what is regarded as the truth, comes to the child as a statement of tradition, but rarely or ever is fully in accord with the formal traditions.

The child, having to learn these lessons, to assimilate them and try to understand and apply their meaning, in the light of his previous experience, handicapped by his limited comprehension and inability to think critically, takes over what he hears and what it means to him. Thus each child establishes his own peculiar interpretation of beliefs and assumptions, his own idiomatic version of cultural traditions, and tries to see and think and act accordingly toward the world of events and people. In this individual version, the child may incorporate many misunderstandings, misconceptions, confusions and conflicts which he will reconcile as best he can and often continue to believe the rest of his life.

Since to live in the cultural world each individual must impose his concepts and assumptions upon the geographical environment, to give it the meanings of his traditions, each individual, of necessity, utilizes this personal version to build up the symbolic world of meanings and values in which he will live. Thus we may say that each individual lives in a "private world" of his own, which he creates himself.

This "private world" is not some occult realm inside the

child; it is the "life space" he creates in the environing world of nature and people, as selectively perceived, organized and interpreted by the child according to what he has learned and how he feels. Thus the child creates his "private world" in the life space he establishes and in that life space he engages in continual transactions with situations, with animals and plants, and with other persons, always according to the peculiar meanings and values, promises or threats as he himself has selectively perceived and interpreted them.

This private world, being derived from cultural traditions, will embody the general pattern of those traditions and so will resemble the "private world" of other members of the group. But each "private world" will be different and each individual will see events, interpret situations and traditions, and react to people in his own individualized way.

This process of building up and maintaining our "private world" of seeing, hearing, thinking, believing, acting and feeling in our own way is what we call the personality—a dynamic process that never ceases so long as the individual lives, since he must actively maintain his life space at all times.

The neurotic's private world often necessitates heavy, and sometimes unbearable, efforts to maintain and defend it, since it is organized with discrepant and incongruous patterns and conflicting emotions or is oriented to goals and purposes that are unachievable and self-defeating.

This conception of personality as a dynamic, active process which the human organism develops, offers an escape from the long accepted splitting up of the individual into body, mind and soul. Today we may regard the human being as, at one and the same time, (1) an organism engaged in functioning in his internal environment through direct intercourse with the geographical environment of nature, (2) a member of a society engaged in living within the patterns and prescriptions of his group life and institutions, (3) a culture bearer who has learned to interpret and deal with nature and himself according to the traditions of his group, and finally (4) a unique personality who carries on, along with his other functions, those of maintaining and defending his individualized version of culture and of social order.

Personality then is this uniquely combined interplay of living in different environments which we can begin to understand without invoking any superhuman, subjective, supernatural or other mystical assumptions about man or nature.

Moreover, we may view personality not as a thing or an entity but as a continuing process—a dynamic process or way of functioning, living, behaving, including the activity of language which involves the use of ideas and concepts and also of talking to ourselves (silently and with various kinds of images and fantasies). Indeed, human living, as pointed out earlier, is unique because man lives by ideas and beliefs, creates and maintains a symbolic world of meanings and values, of goals and purposes to and by which his learned conduct is oriented. Man also develops an image of the self as he does of everything he attends to, and this image of self is the center or focus of his private world, where he continually talks to himself.

Thus the child learns to think about himself, to develop an image of the self according to what he is told and how he is treated by others, especially by his parents who tell him he is good or bad, lovable or unlovable, worthy or unworthy, capable or incapable. This image of the self becomes fixated as the child grows older and he organizes his private world around that image of the self. What he will do or be, how he will feel toward others, what he will aspire to, will all be governed primarily by that image of the self. Only as he changes his image of the self (as may occur in adolescence or in therapy), can he reconstruct his life space and redefine the world and its meanings, since his personality process operates to maintain that image of the self and the life space.

Insofar as our traditional teachings have given us an image of the self as evil, with a body we must distrust, we have developed private worlds that are often in conflict with our ethical aspirations and so lead us into continual self-defeat.

Personality, therefore, is not to be regarded as a psychic entity, nor as a collection of separate parts or factors, but as this unique way by which each individual human organism learns to live in the cultural environment, to accept and carry on traditions but always as an individual, with his own private thoughts and feelings, his own personal reveries and day dreams, and his own peculiar feelings by and for which he maintains his "private world."

This conception of a "private world" carries on and extends the basic ideas previously expressed. Different complexes of energy have appeared in the world as different constellations or patterns made possible by the underlying space-time and energy transformations. In the organic world different kinds of plants and animals have evolved as expressive of the many possible ways in which the living processes could be structuralized and carried on in the same geographical environment.

Man appeared as a late arrival on this scene, with an unusual degree of flexibility and plasticity, a capacity for creating a human way of life quite different from all other organisms yet still natural and always in the setting of nature. This same capacity for selective awareness and patterned conduct becomes further specialized and differentiated in each individual man where it operates as the personality process whereby each one builds up his own "private world" which in turn is a selected version of the cultural traditions about the geographical world of nature and man and his society.

Today we are realizing that every perception—whatever we see, hear or otherwise experience—is what we conceive; we see and hear only what we have learned to see and hear, and to expect, as we learned to give meaning to what we experience and as we extend these meanings. Thus our ideas, beliefs, assumptions, colored by our feelings, organize our experience, giving every event its significance and relationship to other events, according to what we believe and assume it to be and to mean. Each culture gives its members these patterns of belief and of awareness, so that each one will behave according to the *eidos* and *ethos* of the culture.

Thus if we develop a new idea, formulate a new conception, immediately we have changed the world to the extent that the new idea changes what we perceive, what inferences we will draw and how we will react to what we perceive, infer and expect. Hence the introduction of new ideas, of new ways of thinking and new criteria of credibility, which question or supersede the old, immediately starts a process of reorientation which *may* go on indefinitely, as the new idea operates in ever widening areas of experience. Sometimes a new idea is accepted but rigidly confined to one area of experience, as we have accepted modern technology without altering our other ideas and ways of thinking.

We can see this process of reorientation in the field of art, where every creative picture or sculpture discloses new dimensions, new forms, new shapes, new relationships which we had not previously observed. Thereafter we begin to see the new wherever we look although before we had never been aware of it.

All this is explicable when we realize that it is we who create the cultural world, in which we as human personalities live, by our perception-conception, by our selective awareness, our inferences and expectations which we have developed from our childhood experiences. Then through the continual transactions with the environment and other persons we maintain the life space for our private worlds.

Since our private worlds are organized upon our beliefs and assumptions and the feelings which we developed when we learned those patterns, we cannot easily tolerate any new or different ideas, especially if they touch closely our own personal lives and feelings. We can, if it is necessary, or if it promises advantages, accept a new tool or instrument, a new weapon or mode of transportation and communication, since they involve changes which can be used to maintain and, if needed, defend our customary beliefs and habitual activities. Thus we have accepted new inventions, the products of technology and innumerable gadgets, plus the many comforts and conveniences of "modern living," but we have limited their applications and, so far as possible, their meaning to these practical activities, carefully ignoring or even rejecting their implications and cumulative consequences for the rest of our lives.

Nothing is more dramatically conflicting than the recently developed modes of thinking and action in science and technology and those used in social and personal living where we cling loyally to anachronistic, even archaic, patterns and stubbornly resist the kind of critical thinking and testing that have made science and technology possible.

Today every intelligent individual is faced with the conflicts in our traditions which he must try individually to reconcile or harmonize. Often these conflicts give rise to acute anxieties as the individual finds it impossible to live without continual perplexity and confusion over these basic assumptions of our traditional culture. These conflicts and anxieties are especially difficult in our human relations where we are confronted with the old theological, legal beliefs and patterns and with our growing concern for human values and fulfillments.

Recent studies of personality development, especially of those whom we call mentally disordered (the insane as legally known) and of those who suffer from various personality difficulties and emotional conflicts (the so-called neurotic), show that many individuals build up "private worlds" that are confused and disorderly, torn by conflicting ideas and beliefs which appear in overt behavior and destructive or self-defeating feelings.

As we learn how these individuals are warped and twisted and prevented from achieving maturity by the way they are treated in childhood, we need no longer be pessimistic about human nature. While some forms of mental disorder are still beyond our present understanding, many can now be recognized as products of early life experience when the individuals were unnecessarily deprived, frustrated, coerced and often terrorized, or faced with threats, insecurity and unreconcilable teachings. They developed private worlds that are disorderly, either antisocial or self-defeating.

It is becoming increasingly evident that each individual personally creates his own personal problems by the way he creates and maintains his life space, as he invested situations, events and other persons with the meanings that make them problematic to him, although others may face those some situations and persons with no such difficulties. The individual not only creates his own problems but he tries to resolve them by the same assumptions and patterns of conduct and feelings that create them, thereby perpetuating his difficulties unless and until he can redefine his life space and escape from this self-defeating repetitive process.

By recognizing the human personality as the latest and most sensitive expression of the plasticity of nature, we may find a new basis for the belief in the value and worth of the individual and for the aspiration toward human dignity. Previously it was believed that the individual derived from supernatural sources whatever value and worth he was accorded. He was seen as possessing a psychic substance or entity, the soul, which was entrusted to him by an all-powerful deity. Whatever dignity the human being had was, as it were, loaned to him from that supernatural source and he, therefore, could claim no innate dignity and worth as a human being.

With the weakening of these older theological beliefs, there is an acute need for a new conception of the individual personality and his relation to society and for a firmer basis for believing in his value and his dignity as the guiding conception of social life.

By viewing the human organism with his mammalian ancestry as a part of nature, sharing the same dynamic processes and exhibiting the same underlying pattern of organization that is operating everywhere from the atom to the stars, throughout the whole universe, man begins to emerge from the former beliefs and misconceptions that taught him to despise his body and to consider human life of little significance save as a preparation for the hereafter. No longer need he assume that he is by nature incapable of developing a way of life that will have meaning and significance in human terms.

Today we are realizing that for a healthy, sane, humanly fulfilling society we must develop healthy, sane, mature and cooperative personalities who can live at peace with themselves in their private worlds and so can live at peace with others.

The immature, disturbed, neurotic personality not only cannot participate in maintaining a healthy, sane society, but is usually driven to actions that are socially undesirable, if not destructive, or so self-defeating that he cannot contribute to the social tasks.

Man is building a new image of the self that reflects the new knowledge and understanding of nature and these new insights into human nature. They give promise of help in achieving the aspirations and values he has long cherished but has been unable to attain, largely because he could not believe in himself and in his children.

VII

Our New Outlook on Life

Ⅰ F WE GRASP THE NEW CONCEP-
tions outlined in the preceding chapters and reflect upon their
meaning, we will see how far-reaching are the changes taking
place in our cultural traditions. As pointed out at the beginning
of this book, we are creating today a new climate of opinion,
with radically different assumptions about nature and man, and
with criteria of credibility which are altering what we can and
will believe and accept as our basic assumptions and our new
convictions in all human living.

These are not *The Truth* or final judgments. As pointed
out earlier, they are expressions of a new and more fruitful way
of thinking about nature and man, which provide more productive ways of ordering and interpreting experience, of formulat-

ing our relations as human beings to the universe. They are, however, only the more recent steps in the endless human adventure of making human life more meaningful and significant as man learns to understand nature and human nature.

In every culture, as pointed out in Chapter IV, people have had their own beliefs about the universe, how and by whom it was created and operated, what made things happen, how nature was to be understood, and so on. In our Western European tradition the belief in a single act of creation, by divine fiat, has long been central in our theological teachings. Along with this has been the conviction that divine intervention for man's good or for his punishment could and did take place; that divine intercession could modify or block the operation of natural events so that man could through prayer and supplication alter what would otherwise occur, just as his failure to be good and obedient could provoke catastrophes of volcanic eruption, earthquakes, plagues and epidemics or divine annihilation (*e.g.*, "The Deluge").

These beliefs are survivals of an ancient animistic tradition which has for so long directed human thinking about the universe, making man believe he was at the mercy of unseen but all-powerful deities and that he lived in a world that was ruled by whimsical and unpredictable powers.

As an escape from this conception, scientific studies and formulations have, since the days of Copernicus and Galileo, sought for order and regularity in nature. It was the great achievement of these pioneering and courageous thinkers to reveal order arising from actual or seeming disorder. They showed that the universe was larger than man had previously believed and that it operated in an orderly predictable way as shown by the regularity in the movement of the planets and other celestial activities.

Moreover, scientific study also showed that we need not invoke spirits or special forces from behind (*vis a tergo*) to account for the movement of objects or particles. These acted according to their size or weight (mass), their previous state or motion (inertia), and their observed motions could be mathe-matically calculated and predicted.

Up to about 1900 these astronomical and physical concep-tions provided the major assumptions about the universe. They were expressions of what was called a mechanistic or materialis-tic theory of events and assumed that whatever happened was rigidly determined, even though we could not always trace out the sequence of cause and effect through which all events were determined.

These beliefs and these assumptions were immensely pro-ductive, giving rise not only to a comprehensive body of find-ings and theories we call astronomy and physics, but also to all the varied tools, machines and engineering techniques of our industrial world.

But, however satisfying and helpful these scientific achieve-ments were, they provided only a limited understanding of other aspects of nature. Thus physics and astronomy were per-plexed by a number of unexplainable deviations or departures from exact cause and effect, and the life sciences—biology, psy-chology, the social sciences—were unable to proceed beyond a certain point in applying these mechanistic conceptions and methods of investigation.

Within the past fifty years, with the rise of nuclear physics and the development of relativity, of the concept of space-time, curved space and the growing understanding of the structure and operation of the atom, a new and very fruitful advance has been made in scientific thinking.

Today we can begin to conceive of a universe that exhibits both the cause and effect relationships, the deterministic pat-terns, the large-scale regularities of order arising from disorder (such as the orderly behavior of a gas which arises from the dis-orderly behavior of millions and millions of molecules). Many events are predictable as physics and astronomy have shown, but we must also recognize the unpredictability of small-scale events, such as the emission of electrons in definite quanta, the relativity of all observations and measurements, and the lack of hard, rigid boundaries. In brief, the universe also is being revealed as having hitherto unbelievable plasticity, flexibility and immense potentialities which provide for the first time an approach to living events and social life as well as an understanding of atomic events and how to transmute the elements and produce fission of the atomic nucleus.

With these new conceptions, we are being compelled to alter our former beliefs about the universe, giving up the lingering animism (which still survived in disguised form even in some scientific thinking) and revising many of the mechanistic convictions of the past few centuries of scientific investigation.

In this discussion we cannot explore all the many implications of these recent scientific developments which have brought a new and radically different way of thinking about nature, supplementing and modifying much of the former scientific beliefs and, what is more important, enlarging our conceptions of the universe, its ways of operating and consequently giving us a larger, broader and more fruitful approach to the ancient questions of the nature of the universe.

Probably the most far-reaching implication of these new conceptions of the universe is revealed in a new time perspective that is beginning to be developed. For centuries we have believed the world was created in a brief interval of a few days, only a short time ago, as described in the Book of Genesis. We have, therefore, viewed the world as having a very brief history and as coming to an end in the relatively near future. Human life viewed in this narrow and abbreviated time perspective was but an interval, an interlude between birth and death, in which the human soul was being tested to see if the individual had the virtue, the fortitude, the obedience which would merit his eternal salvation, or if he was to suffer eternal punishment for his failure to live up to divine commandments.

This short time perspective fostered the provisional ethics of our traditional teachings and shaped our goals and values to an equally limited, restricted set of values—of striving for individual personal salvation during a brief lifetime of no value in itself in a world which was believed to be deceptive and antagonistic to all human strivings.

Today we are beginning to enlarge our time perspective as we realize the universe has been in existence and has been evolving for billions of years and will probably continue for an indefinite future. Thus we must begin to think in terms of the long-term human adventure in which we are privileged to participate and for which we must formulate a long-term ethic.

It will take years of reflection to reveal the far-reaching possibilities of these new conceptions and new ways of investigating and understanding events. The more we grasp these new ideas, the more clearly we realize that nature is not a gigantic machine, not a collection of inert particles, of "atoms blindly running," not a "materialistic" world, without meaning, purposes or goals.

Until recently the basic assumptions about the universe were essentially static—inert particles were moved by other particles or by heat agitation and gravitation, so that exchange of heat and motion were the only processes believed to be operating. Today science conceives of a dynamic world, in which the basic dynamics of atoms and electrical charges within and between atoms operate to produce events.

Much of the customary denunciation of science has become meaningless and irrelevant since science today is no longer mechanistic or materialistic, but is dynamic, with full recognition that the processes of nature are not rigid and fixed but capable of amazingly subtle and delicate operations, of creative activity, as shown in transmutation of elements, the creation of new synthetic substances, of biological equivalents for many organic products, all expressive of these newly revealed dynamic processes in the universe.

Thus if we are aware of what is happening today, we must try to grasp this new conception of the universe as a dynamic, ever changing, but self-regulating, totality. We must realize that there is order and regularity, cause and effect, in certain convergent events, that everything that exists does so by unceasing activity which alone makes existence possible. Then, too, we must recognize the underlying processes that do not conform to the cause and effect formula of convergent events, but are not orderly, regular. These are the divergent events, unpredictable, dynamic and productive of new sequences, as Irving Langmuir has explicitly pointed out and Schroedinger has further discussed.

Along with these changed conceptions we must also recognize that the universe has been operating for an inconceivable period of time in which continual changes have been taking place, all produced by the dynamics of the universe itself. Moreover, these processes in our dynamic universe have given rise to a multiplicity of organized structures, configurations, persistent patterns which exhibit orderly, self-regulating activities or functions as in plant and animal organisms. In the course of evolution the universe has developed a "natural teleology," as F. J. E. Woodbridge pointed out years ago and as we can plainly see when we observe the purposive striving and functioning of organisms that have been evolved as an expression of the potentialities of our dynamic universe.

As we contemplate these recently formulated ideas and their implications, it is obvious that we can no longer accept many of our older beliefs. But, we are faced again with all the challenging urgency of the question, what is nature, how was it begun and developed. To that question we must reply by making some assumptions, by formulating some beliefs that we cannot prove or disprove, but which we can accept as more credible than the old. Already we have the basis for new assumptions about the nature of the universe, man's place in that universe, his place in and relation to his society, and human nature and man's image of the self. Here we see how modern science is providing what religious beliefs have always sought, a coherent set of beliefs about the universe and man.

Thus, as described in Chapter III, on the basis of recent studies of the human organism, we can today see that man is *in* nature, not an un-natural or supernatural being created and placed outside of nature. Also, we can now say that nature is *in* man.

As pointed out, the human organism in its internal environment exhibits similar dynamic processes of orderly operation and self-regulation, but also divergent activities with variations and creative purposive activities, not only biologically, but psychologically and socially.

Here we are finding a more acceptable conception of man's own body than the ancient attitude of contempt for his own organism. The older beliefs we have long accepted were that man was evil and perverse due largely to his organism with its animal-like functions, its low and degrading impulses and feelings.

In accordance with these beliefs, we have felt that our bodies were a burden and a handicap, and that everything below the neck was more or less unclean, obscene and despicable. Indeed, many people are brought up to feel nothing but shame for their own bodies, hiding it even from their own sight, with a feeling of disgust particularly for their own genitals and reproductive organs.

This has given rise to a persistent conflict in the individual, an uneasy and often guilty feeling about his organic functions, eating, elimination, sexual intercourse, with a strong resistance toward teachings about hygiene, preventive medicine and how to live more wholesomely and effectively. Thus these ancient beliefs and feelings about the human organism have been self-defeating and have often led to conduct which was expressive of guilt and disgust toward the individual's own body and that of others.

Today the new understanding of man's organism, of this marvelous internal environment in which we can observe the same basic natural processes as in the outside environment, is bringing us release from these older self-defeating and conflicting ideas and feelings. We can now begin to accept our organism, to be proud of our mammalian functions, to feel our sense of kinship and belonging to nature with an ancestry going back millions of years through mammalian and pre-mammalian organisms.

We recognize that the human body is capable of developing an extraordinary variety of illnesses, dysfunctions, pathologies and malignancies like cancer. But we are also realizing that, given adequate care, nutrition, and other requirements for organic living, the human body can exhibit robust health, vigorous full functioning, and can provide many fulfillments. What these potentialities produce for good or ill can be increasingly guided and controlled.

Indeed, for the first time we have a hopeful and truly inspiring conception of man as an organism with hitherto unrecognized potentialities through which he can attain many of his long cherished needs and aspirations, and avoid many of the ills and disorders he has suffered in the past.

The growing understanding of man as a mammalian organism, showing the same basic organ systems and functions as other mammals, has made possible the development of modern medicine. Indeed, without such basic similarity, experimental studies on animal subjects leading to improved medical care would be meaningless if not impossible. Thus we are benefiting directly from this newer conception of man and from the development of public health and preventive medicine which have already reduced or eliminated many of the major hazards to health and longevity and give promise of providing ways to vigorous full functioning for everyone.

As we learn to accept our own organisms, to feel at home in our own skins, to have pride in our bodies and confidence in our biological-organic capacities, we experience a great relief—release from the older feelings of guilt and shame about our organic functions, from the older anxieties about our own bodies. Now we can begin to apply the growing knowledge of human functions to develop a wholesome, full functioning way of living, respecting the integrity of the human body beginning at birth.

No one who becomes familiar with the processes of human growth, development, maturation and aging from conception to death can, unless too badly distorted by the old teachings, fail to be impressed by the orderliness and marvelous complexity of what is taking, or has taken, place in his own body or in his children. Yet each organism is unique. As we grasp the basic conceptions of organic functioning, as now being formulated, we begin to realize what a great privilege it is to be a human being, to live in and as an organism.

Along with this new orientation and change in feelings toward the human organism comes an awareness of how much of the degradation and humiliation, the appallingly sub-human living of many people stems from older beliefs about the human body which also often serve to justify what is done to many members of society.

It is worth noting that, despite the long accepted belief in the dignity of man, these self-defeating beliefs about the human body have been accepted and approved even when they lead to actions by individuals toward their own bodies or to treatment of others which disregard or deny human dignity and violate all our ethical aspirations.

Perhaps the greatest change that will come from these new conceptions of the human organism and the respect for the body and its functions will be the abandonment of much of the older teachings about sex. Man's sexual organs and functions and desires have for centuries been regarded as essentially evil, dirty, obscene, and children have been taught to feel disgust and shame for one of the most marvelous functions and one of the great potentialities of the human organism. It is now being shown that this feeling of self-loathing and of guilt about sex is conducive to many of the worst forms of personality distortion and of sexual misbehavior which injures, degrades or otherwise undermines the dignity of the act and of others, especially of women.

It is worth recalling that we have been accustomed to call various forms of human sexual activity bestial, animalistic and similar terms indicating that such actions are what sub-human organisms do. Actually it is clear that no animal, except man, acts in these ways, since all other organisms (not in captivity) are free from the warping of sexual impulses that we see expressed in human sexual perversities and distortions. Only man who lives by ideas and imagination exhibits, when his sexual functioning has been frustrated or twisted, these many forms of distorted sexual activity, also the sex vicariates and surrogates, many of which are not perverse but are the normal variations invented by man to intensify and embellish his sexual functioning.

It is also to be remembered that sexual relations among all organisms except man are limited to the period of heat or fertility in the female and so serve only the purpose of procreation. Only man has transformed sex into an interpersonal relation, "another language" as Dr. James S. Plant called it, thus making sex another resource for human living, for communication, and for fulfillment of other than procreational needs. To limit sex relations to intercourse for procreation, as long prescribed by some authorities, is to reduce human sexuality to the level of organisms and make the woman a sex object to be used, often compelled to childbearing, against her own desires.

By learning to accept our own bodies and to respect their functions and capacities, we can begin to develop a sex ethic which will, we can confidently predict, both reduce the present immense toll of human self-defeat and conflict and exploitation of others and also lead to a richer, fuller, saner way of living, with improved interpersonal relations between men and women.

Here it is important to recognize that the older teachings about sex were sanctioned by the older conception of the universe and man's place therein which have asserted that man was outside of nature and therefore must despise and reject his organic impulses and sexual functions. Over the centuries these distorted and degrading beliefs about human sexuality and the unclean nature of sex and of the body have controlled the human acceptance and expression of sex.

With the growing rejection of these older beliefs and the abandonment of this ancient conception of man's body, the way is opening for a reformulation of our basic conceptions on this subject and the development of a new and humanly more constructive set of ideas and of feelings toward the human body and sexual functions. We are becoming ready for such new formulations because we are freed from the older beliefs and the sanctions which forbade us even to question the older teachings, and are recognizing the need for a better sex ethic.

One of the major tasks ahead is to set our long-term goals, to formulate our human ethics in terms of the new time perspective discussed earlier, and of this new conception of human potentialities. For this we must learn to do what may be called human planning, not just social, economic or national planning, and to evaluate whatever we do in terms of its relation to the ongoing processes of human development and to human potentialities in the long-term future.

In this way we may find again some direction and guidance to purposive striving, to the pursuit of goals which will give human living renewed meaning and larger significance as the older beliefs once did in the time of their formulation.

As we try to clarify our ideas on this problem, we can today benefit from the growing understanding of what human culture means and does. For centuries we have believed that culture was a superhuman system or organization, something given to man from on high or by a transcendent figure, "the culture hero." This viewpoint emphasized that cultural traditions were to be accepted as beyond man's reach or even his critical thinking, except for those brief periods in Greece and in Europe described in the first chapter.

Today we can assert with full conviction that culture is a human creation, man's attempt to order and pattern his personal life and to provide for orderly group or social living. Moreover, we are recognizing the dynamics of culture, of how it operates in human beings, who learn to think, to act, to feel according to what they are taught in childhood and youth when they are culturized by parents and others.

This indicates that culture is not a superhuman system, final and unchanging, beyond man's reach and control; also, it shows that we can and do change culture by modifying what we think and do and feel and what we teach and how we rear our children.

Again, this new viewpoint, when once grasped, brings an immense relief and a feeling of freedom we have never had before under the older beliefs in a supernaturally imposed culture, sanctioned by immemorial tradition.

Today we are privileged not only to examine all our traditions critically but to change our archaic beliefs; indeed, unless we deliberately close our eyes and ears and reject the new knowledge and the new understanding, we cannot avoid being critically aware of how much our traditional assumptions have become progressively incredible and inadequate, frequently misleading and defeating our efforts to live wisely.

Moreover, we are finding in this critical approach a basis for new hope and a more courageous approach to living because we are recognizing that through cultural change man may continue indefinitely to evolve, to modify and improve his human way of life, and, more importantly, to explore and develop the full potentialities of human nature.

As pointed out in Chapter IV, each culture has selectively recognized and cultivated some of our human potentialities and ignored or repressed others. It seems clear that up to the present no one culture has fully accepted human nature and tried to foster the development of men, women and children beyond its often rigid conception of what is good or desirable for their ways of thinking and feeling.

We may, therefore, look ahead and conceive of an endless process of exploration and development as man, guided by the ever increasing knowledge of his potentialities, his mammalian functions and human capacities, and by an ever clearer realization of how they may be used productively, goes on evolving in an ever changing world.

It is eloquent testimony to our human anxiety in the face of what has for so long been regarded as an unfriendly, hostile and untrustworthy world and an equally untrustworthy human nature, that almost everywhere man has been fearful of change. To maintain his traditions and his institutions without modification, to remain loyal to the past, has been long regarded as the height of human wisdom, the only safe and rational way to live.

This deep-seated fear of change, reinforced by resistance to alteration on the part of those who exercised power and had control over social life, is slowly being dispelled as we learn to think in terms of change, evolution, development in nature, in man, in culture and in social order. As soon as we accept this reorientation and realize that only by continual change can we survive and continue to seek the basic goals of human life, we will reorganize our education in the home and school to produce personalities who will feel secure and courageous because they have learned to think and feel dynamically.

Here again we see how a broad over-all reformulation of our beliefs and assumptions about nature and man are essential to any effective alteration in education and how these new ideas provide the reassurance and the sanctions for giving up the older ideas and accepting the new.

Learning to think of culture in this way, as man's own creation, as the process by and through which he makes human living meaningful and significant, gives another great impetus toward this large reconstruction. Heretofore, we have regarded as culture something outside man to which he has been compelled to adjust. Now we are discovering that culture is *in* man and man is *in* culture, in that culture functions in and through human activity—what people believe, the way they think, act, feel and aspire.

While man has created buildings, monuments, art and literature, tools and techniques, these are all the expressions of his ideas, his assumptions and his feeling and his aspirations. Apart from the living human being, they have no meaning or purpose. It is very difficult for archeologists digging up the remains of dead civilizations to understand what they find, because these objects, ruins, etc., are inert and meaningless except as they can be interpreted in terms of their use, their relations to a way of human living and the beliefs of the long dead people who made and used them.

Thus we must free ourselves of the older conception of man *and* culture as separate entities and try to grasp this two-way, reciprocal or circular, dynamic relation: that man himself carries in his organism-personality his ideas and feelings which we call culture. By translating these into functional patterns and social conduct, into buildings, tools, weapons, art and a way of group living, man and his fellows both create and are responsive to culture. Hence, we must think of culture *in* man and of man *in* culture, as we are learning to think of nature *in* man and of man *in* nature.

With this reorientation and the acceptance of this circular, reciprocal interrelationship, we will find fruitful leads toward the reconstruction of culture and, concurrently, the alteration of human conduct and social order.

While many are becoming ready, however hesitatingly, to consider this change of thinking about culture, they find it difficult to take the further step of revising our traditional ideas about society or social order.

The long accepted beliefs about social order have been based upon the assumption that social order is above and outside man who is required to accept and conform to its prescriptions and prohibitions. Earlier beliefs emphasized the supernatural origin of society, as established by divine power and subject to divine commandments. Later social theorists, influenced by the contemporary scientific thinking, continued this belief in social order as outside and beyond man, but located it in nature, as a mechanism operating by forces just as Newton conceived of the celestial system as a large scale mechanism operating by forces acting at a distance, such as gravitation.

Thus today not only social scientists, but ordinary citizens, are still loyal to this assumption that there are social-economic-political mechanisms or systems, each with its special operating forces and laws, above and beyond human control, to which man must give submissive obedience. It is worth noting that both radical theories and the conservative-reactionary theories agree in asserting that social life is controlled by superhuman forces or trends or historic processes which man cannot (or must not) change or try to modify (except to hasten or retard).

Our contemporary social theories are, therefore, essentially defeatist, emphasizing human impotence in the face of these assumed mechanisms, forces, trends, etc., which operate above and beyond human activities, limiting, coercing and blocking human life except as man obediently submits to their operation.

What now appears, as discussed in Chapter V, is that social order is a human creation, man's own historically developed attempts to organize and regulate and carry on group living. Social order is *in* man, just as nature and culture are in man, and, reciprocally, man is *in* the social order he creates and maintains and changes.

Only as children are indoctrinated with the accepted beliefs and taught to utilize the group's approved rituals, ceremonies, symbols and practices, can social order be maintained. When so reared, each child grows up to act toward others as expected by them and to expect what others do and say to him. He learns to carry on all his life activities within the patterns and framework of what we call social institutions which he, along with others, sustains and operates and which in turn regulate and limit what he can and will do and how he will do it. Obviously each individual does this in his own individualized ways as he uses the group sanctioned patterns of legal, economic, political, social activities.

No one individual himself created social order nor can any one alone maintain or change society. It is produced by the patterned, purposive activities of all members of the group and it is perpetuated by the education and training of children to live within the confines and to utilize the practices and privileges of their group sanctioned ways of social life.

This circular conception, as pointed out previously, is essential to an understanding of the dynamic processes of nature and culture and social order. We have difficulty in grasping this new way of thinking because we have for long thought in static terms; that nothing happened or could happen except by the operation of some potent cause acting upon a more or less passive object which then was changed into or made to yield the effect. This is the same conception behind the belief in a coercive historic process that operates as a superhuman power over human living.

These ideas were great achievements, significant steps in man's attempt to understand events, to find some order and meaning in what appeared, and to a large extent actually was, a disorderly world. But just as these venerable ideas of our traditions (and of the traditions of other people), which we still cherish, were products of the ablest and wisest thinkers in their day, who replaced still older ideas with their own, so we today are privileged to contribute to this ages-old endeavor by formulating and applying the newer understandings and replacing the old with more credible assumptions.

As we learn to see ourselves in a longer time perspective and to recognize that, as heirs to the past, we in turn are the creators of the future, we can become less timid and anxious, more courageously ready to accept new conceptions, especially since they offer what we so urgently need today, a forward looking, constructive way of resolving our contemporary confusions and conflicts, not passively submitting to supposed forces, trends or superhuman historic processes.

While social order is *in* man and man is *in* social order, in many societies there are a few individuals and groups who are in control of what is done and how social life is conducted. These are the individuals who exercise what is called power— political-economic-ecclesiastical-social; they use different institutions and practices to dominate and exploit others to maintain their property and privileges and to resist changes which, however urgently desired by many, they will not permit. In some societies, those in power are engaged in coercing all others to conform to the "blueprints" they are trying to impose as *the* answer to all social problems.

In the face of the "vested interests" today, there are many different kinds of revolutionary movements, ranging from the passive resistance led by Gandhi to the violent upheavals in other countries. In between there are many "reform" programs which, by use of traditional political institutions, as in England, are more or less gradually reconstructing the economic life of the country, and inaugurating large scale programs for human welfare. In some European countries there have been, and still are, a number of authoritarian regimes which by coercion are both compelling their people to accept certain changes and also are preventing other changes. Each of these dictatorships or coercive governments faces much the same social problems and difficulties which, according to the traditions of the country, each is attempting to meet in its peculiar way.

What seems clear is that each culture has its own methods or procedures for social change and what appears to work in one country may be ineffective and be rejected by the people of another country. These alien methods do not operate since they do not accept the beliefs and assumptions and the feelings of the society into which they are being introduced and hence do not produce the expected results.

But it should be recognized that in all of these countries change takes place, if and as it occurs, *in* people, in what they believe, expect and feel. This is clearly shown by the reliance upon force, violence and coercion, since those who seize power or have control of the government realize that no alterations are effective until people accept the new, not only passively, but by altering their ideas and giving up the older beliefs and practices.

It is to be remembered that in every government today, and especially in the authoritarian regimes of the past thirty-odd years, those in control have expended enormous amounts of time, energy and money on propaganda designed to win acceptance of their programs. If social change, including economic and political alterations, were not dependent upon what people believe, these efforts and expenditures would not have been made.

Most of the progaganda is an explanation and defense of the regime and also strong criticism and denunciation of other peoples and other regimes. Even in those countries which have escaped thus far the more abrupt and dramatic changes, we can see the same efforts to persuade people to think in certain ways, especially to be loyal to the older ideas and expectations which have become progressively unacceptable.

As we learn to think of social order as in people and of people as in social order, we increasingly realize that the simplest and most complicated societies are essentially alike in being maintained by the beliefs, the patterned actions, the feelings and the loyalties of people to their traditions. Moreover, it becomes evident that everyone, no matter how insignificant a role or status he has, is actively engaged in maintaining social order by utilizing the group practices and symbols.

Some indication of how far traditional beliefs, symbols and loyalties have broken down may be seen in the growth of so-called subversive movements in almost every country. This propaganda openly appeals to the citizens of each country to accept the teachings and guidance of another country, repudiating their own government and working actively for its displacement or overthrow. In view of the patriotism that has for so long been expressed in loyalty to ones own group and rejection of the foreigners, this apparently growing readiness to listen to and to accept these alien teachings reveals the extent to which the older patterns of belief and conduct have lost their former strength. As pointed out by Fustel de Coulange, the French historian, patriotism is not so much love of one's country or land as it is love of tradition. Today tradition has become less love-able or tolerable and hence people are becoming susceptible to alien appeals.

This indicates that by authority and coercion or by persuasion and education (these being the two polarized approaches) every member of a group is involved in social change. The societies which hold to the belief in the value of the human personality and in the dignity of man must rely upon discussion, persuasion, free choice and upon education, not only of children and youth, but also of adults, as the only method of social change which does not violate these basic human values and aspirations.

For these free societies it is crucial for their continued existence that people recognize this new way of thinking about social order. Only by conceiving of social order as in people who must be respected and recognizing this inescapable circular reciprocal relationship can they meet the increasing necessity for change without losing their freedom and giving up their cherished aspirations.

So long as people can be persuaded or compelled to think of social order as a superhuman system, mechanism or organization, and to believe that what takes place in a society is the result of large, nonhuman forces and inevitable historic trends to which they must submit, so long will they be exposed to the kind of manipulation and coercion, the authoritarian controls which use people for non-human purposes, such as national power or glory, imperialism, economic supremacy, social aggrandizement, ecclesiastical power or utopian plans and similar forms of exploitation and manipulation of human life.

This new conception of social order and the recognition of the dynamics of social life in the patterned activities of all the individual members of that society marks the same kind of transition in conceptions as in physics. As physics has gone on from the static conceptions of particle physics to the dynamics of quantum physics, it has recognized that the source and the locus of all dynamics is within the atom and the field and, therefore, it has become aware of the great significance of the single electron or individual electrical charge and the transactions among the innumerable other electrical charges in the field. This is the seeming paradox of modern physical theory in that it has become concerned with the single quantum of energy and space-time organization as the way to understand the large-scale activities and process of nature.

In a similar way we are now beginning to realize that only as we can understand the individual member of a society, how he or she functions, thinks, acts and feels within the social field, can we gain any understanding of the large-scale activities and operations of a society. We are focusing, therefore, more and more upon the problems of human relations and seeking more insight into the development and varied expressions of personality.

This, then, brings us to the conception of the individual's "private world," as another expression of the new way of thinking about human beings, viewing them as organisms which have become personalities who are *in* nature, *in* culture and *in* society and, at the same time nature, culture and social order are in them.

As in earlier discussions, this reciprocal relationship becomes explicable so soon as we realize that man as an organism exists and functions through the same basic processes as are operating in the geographical environment of nature. But in man they have reached a greater sensitivity, complexity, stability, than in other organisms. As an organism, man, therefore, participates in the totality of activities which make up nature, just as all other organisms participate in their life activities. Hence, he partakes of all that we call natural. Likewise, his essentially human organism and its functions, including what he does in his internal environment and his intercommunication with the natural environment, contributes to this totality we call nature.

The energy man expends in all his activities, intra-organic and in overt action, is derived from the natural environment of which he is a constituent member and he, therefore, as an organism, can never alienate himself from his natural environment. But, as pointed out, man with his intelligence and imagination and his skillful hands, has attempted to create and develop a human way of life, relying upon ideas and tools and weapons, to set up a special kind of human environment, selectively organized and continually maintained by man himself.

The special environment we have discussed as the cultural and the social environment are man's own creations and, hence, they exist and are maintained by the individual members of the group who are continually engaged in transactions with their environment and with other members of the group in and through these cultural patterns.

Thus every member of the group conforms more or less to the traditional beliefs and practices and by that conformity he maintains the culture. But what is significant about the individual personality is that each one always sees, hears, believes, thinks, speaks, acts and feels in his own idiomatic way. Thus each individual, while existing in the geographical environment, carrying on his life activities in the social environment and in the symbolic cultural environment, actually creates his own "life space" and lives as if in a "private world" of his own. This "private world" arises and is maintained by the highly individualized meanings each one imputes to his "life space" and by the peculiar way he thinks and feels toward that idiomatic world which he selectively perceives and deals with.

There is no break in the sequence of transitions from the natural environment with its dynamic operations to the "private world" and its dynamic operations. The individual as an organism participates in and helps to constitute the geographical environment, the cultural environment and the social environment.

Each member of the group carries on his or her life activities in the established patterns and uses the group sanctioned rituals, symbols and ceremonies of his society to conduct all his human relations, including those which are concerned with utilizing the geographical environment, such as the land and water, plants and animals. By their use of these social institutions and forms, each member of the group, more or less obedient to the requirements and prohibitions of their society, maintains the social order.

By maintaining the culture and the social order, each individual recognizes and accepts this group creation and by so much he is guided, directed, coerced by this larger group organization. Again, it must be emphasized that this is a circular, reciprocal process, what is being called a "feed back": within an organism, an organization or a machine, some of the energy and some of the activities are fed back into or applied to maintaining, guiding and regulating the organism or machine in relation to its surroundings. In that way each "part" contributes to the operation and maintenance of the "whole," which, as an organized totality of activities, thereby operates to guide and direct the activities of the "part." This is what we mean by "organization," no longer to be conceived as an entity or some mysterious whole or power superimposed upon parts or people, but what they, by their transactions with the environment and with other persons, jointly create and maintain.

This way of thinking about organization, and especially about culture and social order, rejects the long accepted beliefs that cultural tradition and social order are superhuman entities to which man was forever subordinated, with supernatural sanctions to compel his obedience. It explicitly asserts that the human being who composes the group is the bearer of cultural traditions and the active agent who maintains social order. This, however, is only one implication of these new conceptions and it must be enlarged to recognize that each individual is a personality who by his individualized, idiomatic way of participating as a bearer of traditions and active participant in social order is the source and locus of all human life and achievements.

Instead of the emphasis upon more or less rigid conformity to a code or authority as an ideal to be sought or imposed upon everyone as essential to social order, we now may recognize, and even encourage, the development of the unique individual since as an idiomatic personality each one will, if encouraged and respected as a personality, not only participate culturally and socially but help to bring about the continual alterations and improvements which are essential to a living, dynamic culture and an advancing social order.

This indeed is a radical break with all our traditional concern for subordinating the individual to society, for seeking to compel everyone to think, believe, act and feel in the same way. Just as physics now realizes that not static or mechanical uniformity but the dynamic and often unpredictable activity of atomic processes make an orderly self-regulating and evolving universe possible, so we are beginning to realize that it is the individual personality, living in his or her "private world," who makes possible an orderly self-governing social life and the maintenance of the enduring values of a culture.

Already this new way of thinking about the individual personality has begun to make a difference in our social life. For the past forty years we have been gradually accepting the idea that the young offender against our laws, the juvenile delinquent, is not a deliberate criminal, a willful rebel intentionally defying our laws, nor a wicked, sinful and graceless soul meriting either or both legal imprisonment and supernatural punishment. Today we realize that these delinquents are the victims of maltreatment or neglect which in childhood prevented them from learning the conduct and the self-regulation for orderly group life. Their life experiences have warped, twisted and distorted their personalities, created an image of self that is self-defeating and disturbing, filling them with persistent feelings of hostility or anxiety that is expressed in their illegal and destructive or self-defeating conduct.

These new approaches to the delinquent are challenging the ages-old beliefs about human nature and the relation of the individual to society and are bringing an increasing awareness of how the "private world" of the individual either fosters or threatens social order.

Thus we must recognize that only wholesome personalities can maintain a wholesome society and only a wholesome society can produce wholesome personalities. This is *not* a vicious circle but the essentially circular process through which individuals and the social life are interrelated. This circular process can be altered by what we do for children and adolescents and by re-education (including therapy) of adults.

We, therefore, are recognizing in the early care and rearing of children in the home, their formal education in the school, how important it is to protect and guide the emerging personality of the child as the only effective way to maintain social order by noncoercive, nonauthoritarian methods. This requires far-reaching changes in the beliefs of parents about children and human nature, and considerable modification in the traditional roles of parents.

It seems clear that as families accept these altered conceptions and put into practice these new ideas and methods, they will produce personalities who as adults will find much of our traditional culture and our long-accepted social practices to be no longer meaningful or tolerable. Such personalities will not only conduct their lives in a different way but they in turn will rear their children according to the new ideas and guide them to different ways of life.

Thus a cumulative process of cultural and social change

will be carried on in which the central theme will be the worth of the individual personality, respect for the "private world" of each individual as essential to the dignity of man, woman and child.

Here again we see what a radical break with our traditions this involves, since for centuries we have been taught that the dignity of man was not his own individual personal worth as an organism-personality bearing traditions and maintaining social order, but only as he possessed and enjoyed what was conditionally entrusted to him by a supernatural power or deity. In this traditional teaching man, as man, had no dignity or worth of his own; it was, so to speak, loaned to him, and he could retain it only on sufferance, subject to the extremes of humiliation, degradation, torture and punishment if he disobeyed divine commandments or even dared to think in any way not sanctioned by the authorities.

Today we are being told that we cannot have a free democratic society, we cannot enjoy civil rights or social privileges, indeed, we can aspire to no human dignity unless we accept these ancient beliefs, submit to authority and conform not only in action but in thoughts and feelings to these largely anachronistic prescriptions.

Much of our traditional religion and philosophy were developed long ago when there was no dependable knowledge of the universe, no understanding of nature and of human nature or of these underlying processes that scientific research is now revealing. Today the older beliefs about the world and about man have become incredible, as archaic as the crude stone knives and axes which early man fabricated as his first tools. These early tools were great achievements at that time, revealing the potential intelligence and the skillful hands which man possesses beyond all other organisms. But they were soon superseded by more refined and efficient tools and weapons in a process of continual refinement and elaboration leading to the amazing tools, machines and weapons of today.

In the same way our early beliefs and conceptions expressed man's first attempts to grasp the kind of world he lived in and to understand its operations. They were a great achievement, testifying to man's imagination and daring vision, especially his conception of man as a specially created creature, having a superior place, outside and beyond nature.

But these venerable beliefs and assumptions are anachronisms in a world where our growing knowledge and understanding shows that these older beliefs are no longer meaningful or credible. Moreover, we are beginning to realize that the new knowledge, as we have just seen, provides a more satisfying and more wonderful conception of nature, giving man a place therein more secure than his often wavering faith in supernaturalism could provide.

But the passing of these older and long-cherished beliefs has made many of us uneasy and troubled. We feel that in giving up these ideas, such as the story of the creation of the world and of man in Genesis, we are losing our religion. And so many of us feel insecure, adrift in a world without guidance or direction. Some are afraid that in giving up the older views, man is being reduced to an insignificant, almost contemptible figure in the great immensity of the universe where once he enjoyed a special place and the protection promised by the older beliefs in an all-powerful deity who ran the world and looked after man.

But this feeling of dismay is but the temporary chagrin of egocentric man who has not yet fully realized what a magnificent prospect lies ahead, once he has freed himself from these survivals of the archaic past and learned to feel at home in the universe as now being understood. Social-cultural change, as nearly as we can now understand, operates by providing alternatives to older beliefs and practices which are progressively accepted as people recognize their meaning and realize they offer a more promising way of attaining their goals and ethical aspirations.

Thus the hope for the future is that we will realize even more clearly that this new way of thinking provides a more credible conceptual framework and offers a more fruitful approach to the human goals and aspirations that for so long have been frustrated by the former beliefs we can now relinquish.

As we look forward through the present-day confusion and the uncertainty which during recent years has almost overwhelmed us, we can find, in these new insights into personality development and expression, the clues to most of our tragic self-defeats. We can see, ever more clearly, how we as a people have built into our "private worlds" the conflicting and discrepant beliefs and the corroding feelings that have over the centuries produced the unhappiness, the despair and the resort to every variety of explanation (or rationalization) to comfort us or to excuse and defend ourselves.

We can see today how these archaic beliefs about nature and man, as translated in the family and child rearing and education, have fostered malign, destructive personalities who have injured, destroyed or sought to dominate others as an expression of their unhappy private worlds, and in doing so have defeated themselves.

Human personalities, caught in the many conflicts of our traditions and beset by the irreconcilable feelings in their "private worlds," have been alternately soothed by traditional explanations and stirred by the exhortations to accept them as challenges to be met by virtuous resignation and submission.

This is so central a belief in our culture, so deeply built into our "private worlds" in childhood, that any questioning of this arouses horror in many of us as impious and sacrilegious. Any who assert their independence of these now archaic beliefs are assailed as atheists, as secular monsters who are striving to destroy all law and order, to undermine and destroy morals and ethics and to provoke divine wrath against our whole society, thereby bringing disaster even to the faithful believers.

But the historical record is clear that every human advance has been opposed and resisted by those who cling loyally to the traditional beliefs and practices whatever they may be. Polytheism, idolatry, animism, human and animal sacrifices to the gods, all the varied beliefs and rituals which at one time were accepted by people as *the* only true religion, have been superseded and replaced.

What can be said with conviction is that those ancient cultures which have perished did not go down to ruin and disappear from being courageous and critical of their traditions. They perished, as nearly as we can discover, with their often bizarre religious beliefs and almost incredible rituals, from trying to maintain unchanged archaic assumptions and practices that had become incredible and lost their meaning for people.

Today we can and must recognize that every religion and every culture is an aspiration, an attempt to create an orderly, meaningful way of life, to interpret nature and man so that human life may have goals and purposes. Each culture and each religion has been an historic development, built upon or superseding a previous body of beliefs and patterns of conduct, a former way of life.

Throughout the centuries, what we call liberal religion has, often slowly and reluctantly, recognized the need for giving up anachronistic ideas and practices and replacing them with new, as the only way to continue striving for its goals and maintaining its values. This is the occasion for liberal religion again to look critically at its teachings and to provide a new set of beliefs that we can accept and utilize in the renewal of our culture and reorientation of our social order.

The criteria we can now utilize is not that of long continued acceptance as if a prolonged history gave any human
creation a final sanction, nor divine revelation and authority,
nor any other of the absolutist practices used to impose a body
of beliefs and to defend them as beyond question.

The criteria we today may apply are our enduring values
and persistent aspirations, understanding culture as man's own
creation, an ongoing and never-ending endeavor to understand
nature and man and to develop a human way of life dedicated
to those values and aspirations. Man's potentialities are a product of that nature which he must endlessly strive to understand
and to live in, at peace with himself and with benefit to nature
and himself, as he pursues his enduring goals of human living.

Thus we can and must critically examine our traditions,
and especially our religious teachings, in terms of the ethics they
foster, and give up many of these older beliefs and long-sanc-
tioned practices as no longer ethically acceptable, because self-
defeating.

This means that much of our traditional religious and
ethical teachings are not good enough since they lead to defeat
of our aspirations, to unnecessary conflicts between and among
persons and within the personality. Moreover, they deny man
the dignity and the worth which he may now enjoy as a human
being, but which heretofore has been denied him, as he has been
required to look to and submissively accept authority. Today,
as our new understanding has shown, we need no longer believe
that man is perverse, evil, or fallen from grace, but can now
assert that human nature is capable of almost any conduct, for
good or otherwise, according as he is reared and educated and
as he develops an image of himself.

It is becoming evident that a free society demands the high-
est standard of personal ethics, of self-disciplined, self-governed
conduct by each individual member who respects not only the
integrity and dignity of others but the dignity of the individual

actor himself. In the non-free societies, the authoritarian re-gimes, the dictatorships, there is little need or opportunity for personal ethics since the individual is required to give submis-sive obedience to authority, to conform to what is required by those who are in charge.

It is also clear that for such a free-self-governing society, no one can be unnecessarily deprived, frustrated, injured, dam-aged, humiliated or otherwise distorted and stunted, because anyone so treated will be unable to bear the burdens of free-dom, incapable of playing his full effective role in maintaining social order. Everyone in the group must be able to respect him-self, to live at peace with himself so that he can and will respect others and live peacefully with his fellows.

As Erich Fromm has pointed out, if we are to love our neighbors, we must be able to love ourselves, since those who cannot respect and accept themselves cannot respect and accept others.

Thus we are confronted with the challenging task of using our new knowledge and understanding, accepting the new in-sights, and developing the new ways of thinking by which we can renew our disintegrating culture and reconstruct our social order, along with the people of all other lands who face the same kind of problem.

This will be opposed and denounced, especially by those who fear change, to whom we can offer not arguments and dis-putes but the invitation to join in an endeavor to raise our ethical aspirations to the level we can now formulate as both desirable and achievable, as we learn to see man *in* nature and nature *in* man. This is the new image man can and must create of himself for guiding his strivings toward the enduring values he cherishes. This is what human nature requires and makes possible as an expression of its immense potentialities.

DATE DUE